100 of the Gre
Film
Songs
Ever

Piano

Wise Publications
part of The Music Sales Group
London/New York/Paris/Sydney/Copenhagen/Berlin/Madrid/Tokyo

Published by
Wise Publications
8/9 Frith Street, London W1D 3JB.

Exclusive Distributors:
Music Sales Limited
8/9 Frith Street, London W1D 3JB, England.
Music Sales Pty Limited
120 Rothschild Avenue, Rosebery, NSW 2018, Australia.

This book © Copyright 2005 by Wise Publications,
a division of Music Sales Limited.
Order No. AM983972
ISBN 1-84609-259-0

Cover photo courtesy of Snap/Rex Features.

Printed in the United Kingdom.

www.musicsales.com

Amapola
(from "First Love")

Words & Music by Joseph M. Lacalle

with a way of whis-p'ring "si Se - nor." _____ Each
from the one his arms were long - ing _____ for. _____ He

night _____ while gui - tars would soft - ly play, _____
vowed _____ he'd re - turn one sun - ny day, _____

the tune seem'd to dance _____ 'round the words that he'd
once more to re - peat _____ what his heart had to

say: _____ A - ma - po - la, _____ my pret - ty lit - tle
say: _____

pop - py,_____ you're like that love - ly flow'r so sweet and

hea - ven - ly._____ Since I found you,_____ my heart is wrapp'd a -

round you,_____ and lov - ing you, it seems to beat a

rhap - so - dy._____ A - ma - po - la,_____ the pret - ty lit - tle

poppy____ must copy its endearing charm from you.____ Amapola,____ Amapola,____ how I long to hear you say I love you. Amalove you.____

D.%.al Fine
Fine

9

Alfie
(from "Alfie")

Words by Hal David
Music by Burt Bacharach

Very slowly, rubato

sure as I be - lieve there's a hea - ven a -

bove, Al - fie, I know there's some - thing much

more. Some - thing ev - en non - be - liev - ers can be - lieve in.

I be - lieve in love, Al - fie.___ With - out true love we just ex -

ist,   Al - fie.   Un - til   you   find   the   love   you've

missed   you're   no - thing,   Al - fie.   When   you   walk   let   your   heart

lead   the   way   and   you'll   find   love   a - ny   day,

Al - fie,   Al - fie.

dim. poco a poco

13

As Time Goes By
(from "Casablanca")

Words & Music by Herman Hupfeld

mat-ter what the prog-ress, or what may yet be proved, The sim-ple facts of life are such they

Liltingly

can-not be re-moved. You must re-mem-ber this, a kiss is still a kiss, a

rit.

a tempo

sigh is just a sigh; The fun-da-men-tal things ap-

ply, As time goes by. _____ And

15

when two lov - ers woo, they still say, "I love you," On that you can re - ly;

No mat - ter what the fu - ture brings, As time goes

by.

Moon-light and love __ songs

nev - er out of date, Hearts full of pas - sion, jeal - ous - y and hate;

Wom - an needs man ___ and man just have his mate, That no one can de -

ny. It's still the same old sto - ry, a fight for love and glo - ry, A

case of do or die! The world will al - ways wel - come

lov - ers, As time goes by. You by.

Angel
(from "City Of Angels")

Words & Music by Sarah McLachlan

arms of_____ the an - gel, fly a - way_____ from here._____

_____ From this dark, cold_____ ho - tel room and the

end - less - ness that you__ fear. You are pulled from the

wreck - age of your si - lent__ re - ve - rie.__ You're in the

arms of the an - gel, may you find some com - fort here.

2. So tired of the here.

You're in the arms of the

Verse 2:
So tired of the straight line
And everywhere you turn
There's vultures and thieves at your back
And the storm keeps on twisting
You keep on building the lies
That you make up for all that you lack
It don't make no difference
Escape one last time
It's easier to believe
In this sweet madness
Oh this glorious sadness
That brings me to my knees.

In the arms of the angel *etc.*

Bang, Bang
(My Baby Shot Me Down)
(from "Kill Bill")

Words & Music by Sonny Bono

All Summer Long
(from "American Graffiti")

Words & Music by Brian Wilson & Mike Love

Because
(from "American Beauty")

Words & Music by John Lennon & Paul McCartney

Beyond The Sea

(from "Beyond The Sea")

Original Words & Music by Charles Trenet
English Words by Jack Lawrence

near be-yond the moon.

I know beyond a doubt, my heart

will lead me there soon. We'll

meet beyond the shore, we'll

Born Free
(from "Born Free")

Words by Don Black
Music by John Barry

Born free, as free as the wind blows, as free as the grass grows, born free to fol-low your heart.

time you look at a star.

Stay free, where no walls di - vide you,

you're free as a roar - ing tide so there's no need to

Born To Be Wild

(from "Easy Rider")

Words & Music by Mars Bonfire

1. Get your mo-tor run - ning,—
(Verses 2 & 3 see block lyric)

head out on the high - way,

look-ing for ad - ven - ture,

in what -

-ev - er comes our way._____ Yeah dar - lin' gon - na

make it hap - pen, take the world in a love em - brace,—

fire all of your guns_____ at once_____ and

ex - plode in - to space._____

Like a true na - tures child _____ we were born, born to be wild ___ we can climb so high ___ I nev - er want to die. _____ Born to be wild, ___

Verse 2:
I like smoke and lightning
Heavy metal thunder
Racing in the wind
And the feeling that I'm under.

Yeah darlin' *etc.*

Verse 3: (𝄋.) — as Verse 1

Bring Me To Life
(from "Daredevil")

Words & Music by Ben Moody, Amy Lee & David Hodges

1. *(Female)* How can you see___ in-to___ my eyes, ___ like o-pen doors?___ Lead - ing you___ down

44

Build Me Up Buttercup
(from "There's Something About Mary")

Words & Music by Tony Macaulay & Michael D'Abo

know that I have from the start._____ So build me up (Build me up) But-

-ter-cup, don't break my heart._ 1. "I'll be
(Verse 2 see block lyric)

ov - er at ten"_ you told me time and a - gain,_ but you're late._ I wait a-

-round and then I run to the door,_ I can't take_ a - ny more, it's not you._

Verse 2:
You are my toy but I could be the boy you adore
If you just let me know
Although you aren't true I'm attracted to you all the more
Why do I need you so?

Baby, baby try to find *etc.*

Cabaret
(from "Cabaret")

Words by Fred Ebb
Music by John Kander

1. What good is sit-ting a - lone in your room?
2. Put down the knit-ting, the book and the broom; it's

"What good is sit-ting all a-lone in your room?___

Come hear the mu-sic play.

Life is a ca-ba-ret, old chum;

in rhythm, accel.

come to the ca-ba-ret." And as for

59

Call Me
(from "American Gigolo")

Words & Music by Giorgio Moroder & Deborah Harry

1. Co - lour me___ your co - lour ba - by, co - lour me your car,___
2. Co - ver me___ with kiss - es ba - by, co - ver me with love.___

a -ny place___ a -ny -where___ a -ny way.___

in my life call me, call me a-ny time at all. Call me,

I love you, if you call me we can share the wine.

Call me.

scat singing

69

Come What May
(from "Moulin Rouge")

Words & Music by David Baerwald

The Crying Game
(from "The Crying Game")

Words & Music by Geoff Stephens

I know _ all there
Instrumental solo

of the cry - ing game._____ I

don't want no more _____ of the cry - ing game. _____

Oh! _____

Diamonds Are A Girl's Best Friend
(from "Gentlemen Prefer Blondes")

Words by Leo Robin
Music by Jule Styne

du - els. But I pre - fer a

man who lives... and gives ex - pen - sive

jew - els! _____

Moderate march, with a lilt

Chorus

1. A
(2. I've)
(3. There)

Optional additional lyrics:

Verse
    A well-conducted rendezvous
    Makes a maiden's heart beat quicker.
    But when the rendezvous is through,
    These stones still keep their flicker.

Chorus
    Romance is divine, and I'm not one to knock it,
    But diamonds are a girl's best friend!
    Romance is divine, yes, but where can you hock it?
    When the fame is gone,
    Just try and pawn a tired Don Juan!

    Some men buy, and some just sigh
    That to make you their bride they intend.
    But buyers or sighers,
    They're such god-damn liars!
    Diamonds are a girl's best friend!

Edge Of Seventeen
(from "School Of Rock")

Words & Music by Stevie Nicks

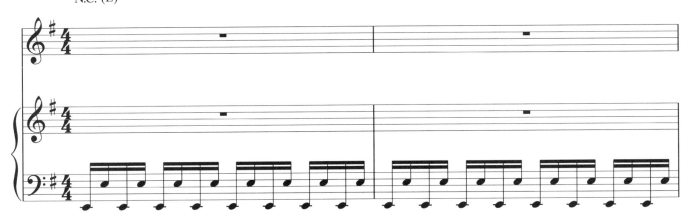

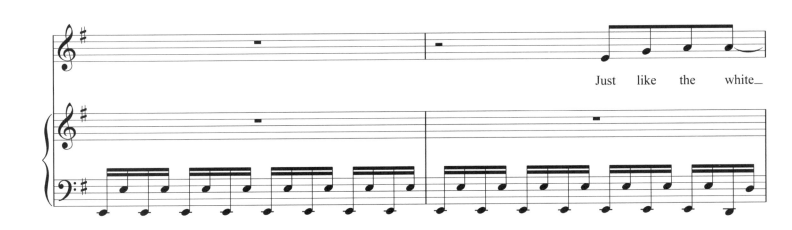

-by then.____

Well, he

seemed bro - ken heart - ed,____

some - thing with - in____

____ him.____

But the mo-

- ment

that I first____ laid

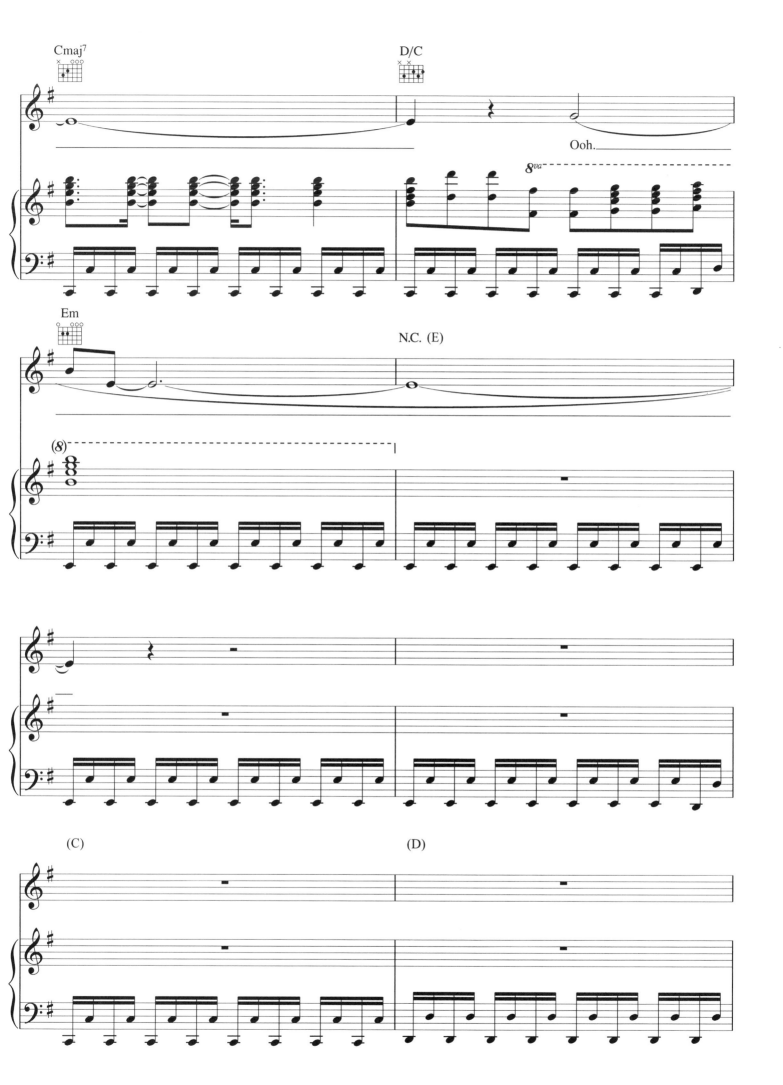

The End
(from "Apocalypse Now")

Words & Music by The Doors

hand,   in a   des - 'prate   land.

Lost   in a   Ro - man____   wil - der - ness of

pain,   and all   the   chil - dren

are in - sane;   all the chil - dren____   are in - sane;

(piano continues to end)

wait - ing for the sum - mer rain.____   There's dan - ger____ on the

edge of town.   Ride the king's   high - way.

Weird scenes in - side the gold mine;___   ride the king's high - way

west,   ba - by.   Ride   the   snake,   to   the

lake,   { The an - cient lake. }   Sev - en   miles   He's
           { The snake is long }   Ride the   snake

old   and his skin is cold_   The West   is   the

best.   The West   is the best.

3

Get here   and we'll do the rest.   The blue bus___

___   is call - ing us.___   Dri - ver, where you tak - ing us?_

⊕ Coda

The end   of   laugh - ter   and   soft lies,   The end   of

nights   we   tried   to   die.   This   is   the   end.___

* The killer awoke before dawn   And he came to the door,
   He put his boots on,   And he looked inside,
   He took a face from the ancient gallery,   "Father?"
   And he walked on down the hall.   "Yes, son?"
                                   "I want to kill you.
   He went to the room where his sister lived,   "Mother I want to ...."
   And then he paid a visit to his brother,
   And then he walked on down the hall.   Come on baby, take a chance with us, (3x)
                                   And meet me at the back of the blue bus.

The End Of The World

(from "Girl, Interrupted")

Words by Sylvia Dee
Music by Arthur Kent

Why does the sun keep on shin - ing? Why does the sea rush to shore?

Don't they know it's the end of the world, 'cause you don't love me an - y - more?

life goes on the way it does! Why does my heart go on beat - ing?

Why do these eyes of mine cry? Don't they know it's the end of the world? It

end - ed when you said good - bye. - bye.

I'm Kissing You

(from "Days Of Thunder")

Words by Des'ree
Music by Des'ree & Tim Atack

I'm_____ kiss - ing you, oh._____

Yeah,_____ yeah,_____ yeah._____

116

Everybody's Talkin'
(from "Midnight Cowboy")

Words & Music by Fred Neil

1. Ev - 'ry - bo - dy's talk - in' at ——— me,

I don't hear a word they're say - in',

on - ly the ech - oes ——————— of ——— my

mind.———————————

through the pour - in' rain,

go - in' where the wea - ther suits my

clothes. Back - in' off of the North-

- East winds, sail - in' on Sum - mer breeze.

And skip-pin' ov-er the o-

cean like a storm.

Woh, woh, woh, woh,— woh,

woh, woh, woh, woh, woh, woh, woh, woh,— woh.

D.%. al Coda

♦ *Coda*

Ev - 'ry - bo - dy's talk - in' at___ me.___

Repeat ad lib. to fade

Ah_____

123

Extreme Ways
(from "The Bourne Identity")

Words & Music by Richard Hall

1. Ex treme ways are back a - gain,___ ex - treme pla - ces I did - n't know.
2. Ex treme ways___ have helped me,___ they've helped me out late at___ night.
(Verses 3 & 4 see block lyrics)

Oh— ba-by, oh— ba-by, like it al-ways does,_____

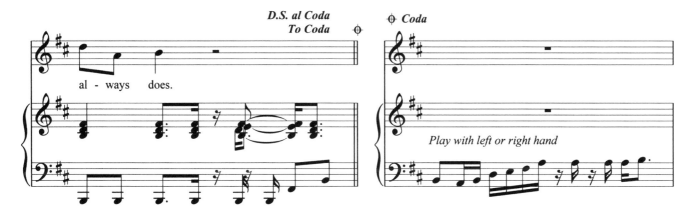

al - ways does.

Play with left or right hand

Verse 3

Extreme sounds that told me
They helped me down every night
I didn't have much to say
I didn't give up the life
I closed my eyes and closed myself
And closed my world and never opened up to anything
It couldn't get me at all

Verse 4

I had to close down everything
I had to close down my mind
Too many things should cover me
Too much could make me blind
I've seen so much in so many places
So many heartaches, so many faces
So many dirty things
You couldn't even believe.

I would stand in line for this
It's always good in life for this.

Oh baby, *etc.*

Eye Of The Tiger
(from "Rocky III")

Words & Music by Frank Sullivan III & Jim Peterik

So man-y times_ it hap-pens too fast,_ You trade your pas-sion for glo-ry._ Don't lose your grip_ on the dreams of the past, You must fight just to keep them a-live_ It's_ the eye of the tig-er, it's the thrill of the fight, ris-ing up to the chal-lenge of our riv-al. And_ the

tig - er.

2. Ri - sin' up,___ straight to the top.___

Had the guts,___ got the glo - ry, Went the di - stance, now I'm

D.S. al Coda

not gon - na stop, just a man___ with his will to sur - vive.___ It's___ the

132

(Everything I Do) I Do It For You
(from "Robin Hood: Prince Of Thieves")

Words by Bryan Adams & Robert John Lange
Music by Michael Kamen

1. Look in-to my eyes, you will see,
2. Look in -to your heart, you will find there's

what you mean to me. Search your heart, search your
noth - ing there to hide. Take me as I am, take my

138

Falling In Love Again
(from "The Blue Angel")

Words & Music by Friedrich Hollander

140

A Fine Romance
(from "Swing Time")

Words by Dorothy Fields
Music by Jerome Kern

should be like a cou-ple of hot to-ma-toes,_____ but
calm-er than the seals in the Arc-tic O - cean,_____ at

you're as cold as yes-ter-day's mashed po-ta-toes._____ A
least they flap their fins to ex-press e-mo-tion;_____ A

fine ro-mance! You won't nes-tle, a
fine ro-mance! With no quar-rels, with

fine ro-mance, you won't wrest-le! I
no in-sults, and all mor-als! I've

But we just "fizz" like parts of a Seid - litz
We don't have half the thrill that the "March of

pow - der._____ A fine ro - mance with
Time" has!_____ A fine ro - mance, with my

no clinch - es, a fine
good wo - man! My strong

ro - mance with no pinch - es, you're
"Aged in the wood" wo - man! You

Footloose
(from "Footloose")

Words & Music by Kenny Loggins & Dean Pitchford

149

feel - in' ___ that time's just hold - in' me down..
tell you ___ that life just ain't pass - in' you by. __

A

Omit 2nd time

D

I'll hit the ceil - in', ___
I'm try - in' to tell you __

D#dim

B7

E

or else I'll tear up this town. ____
it will if you don't e - ven fly.

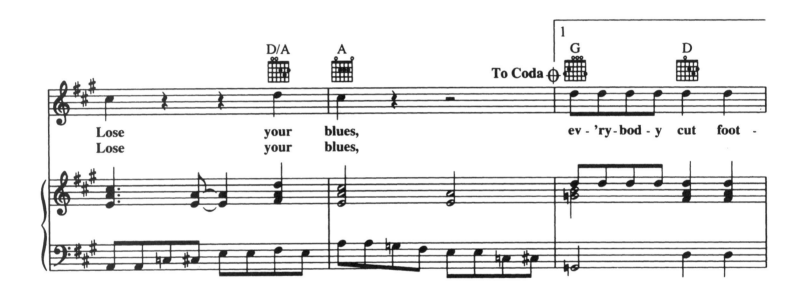

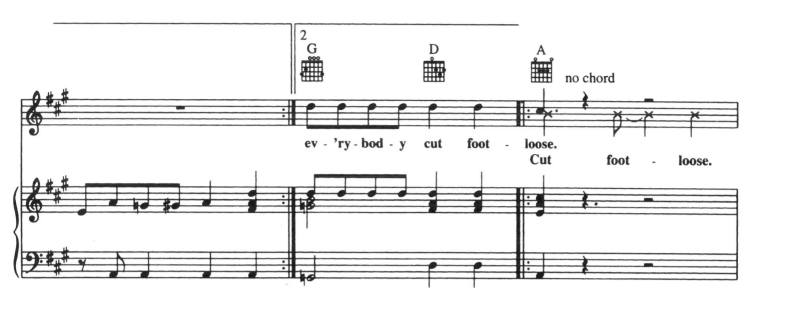

ev - 'ry - bod - y cut foot - loose.
Cut foot - loose.

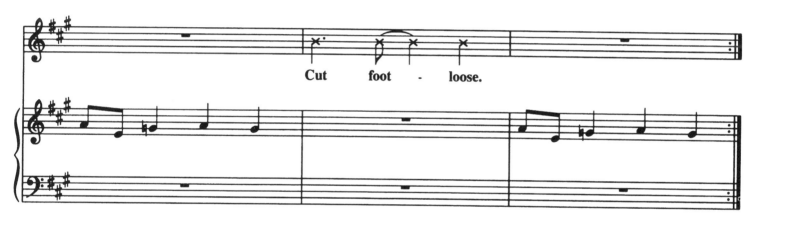

Cut foot - loose.

First, you've got __ to turn __ me a - round, __ sec-ond, and put, __ your feet __

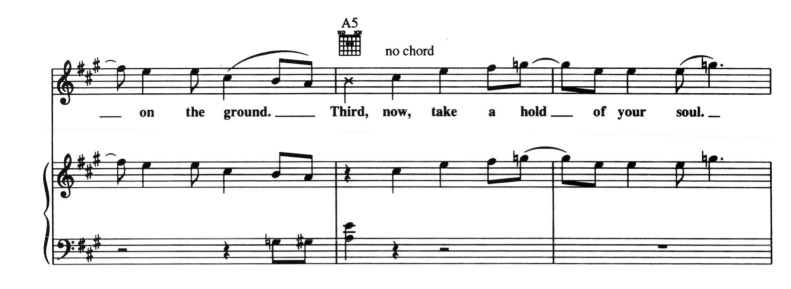

_____ on the ground. _____ Third, now, take a hold _____ of your soul. _____

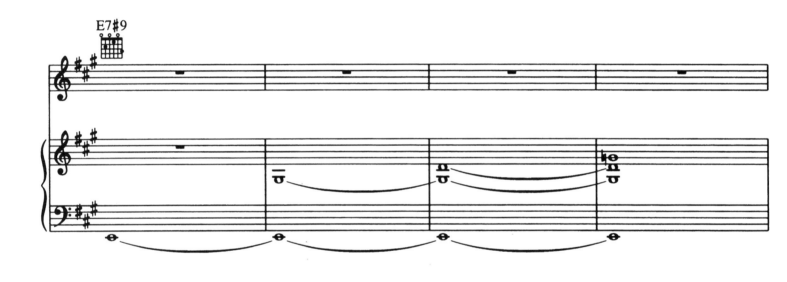

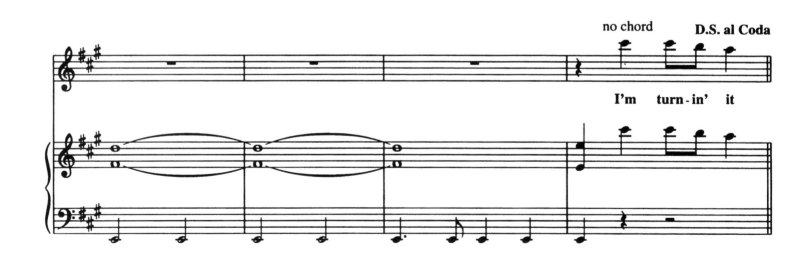

I'm turn-in' it

CODA

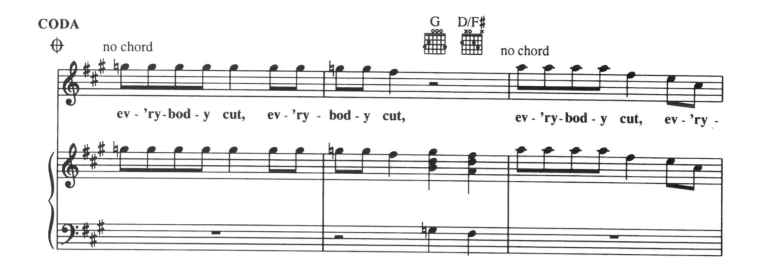

ev - 'ry-bod - y cut,   ev - 'ry - bod - y cut,   ev - 'ry-bod - y cut,   ev - 'ry -

bod - y cut,   ev - 'ry-bod - y cut,   ev - 'ry - bod - y cut,   ev - 'ry-bod - y,

ev - 'ry-bod - y cut   foot - loose.

155

Georgia On My Mind

(from "Ray")

Words by Stuart Gorrell
Music by Hoagy Carmichael

Geor - gia,   Geor - gia,   the whole_ day through._

Just an old sweet song   keeps Geor- gia on_ my mind._

Get Happy
(from "Summer Stock")

Words & Music by Harold Arlen & Ted Koehler

Goldfinger
(from "Goldfinger")

Words by Leslie Bricusse & Anthony Newley
Music by John Barry

Gold - fing - er,___ he's the man, the

Hallelujah
(from "Shrek")

Words & Music by Leonard Cohen

170

The Hands That Built America

(from "Gangs Of New York")

Words & Music by U2

of_____ reach?　　　　　　*Vocal ad lib.*

Happy Together
(from "Adaptation")

Words & Music by Garry Bonner & Alan Gordon

1. I - ma - gine me and you; I do, I think a - bout you

day and night, it's on - ly right___ to think a - bout the girl you love and hold her

tight: so hap-py___ to-geth-er._____ 2. If I should

call you up, in-vest a dime, and you say you be-long to me and ease my
3-5. Me and you, and you and me: no mat-ter how they toss the dice, it had to

mind, i-ma-gine how the world could be so ve-ry fine, so hap-py___ to-
be. The on-ly one for me is you, and you for me: so hap-py___ to-

To Coda ⊕

-geth - er._____
-geth - er._____ (2, 3.) I can't see me
(4.)Ba ba ba ba

High Noon
(from "High Noon")

Words by Ned Washington
Music by Dimitri Tiomkin

A Hard Day's Night
(from "A Hard Day's Night")

Words & Music by John Lennon & Paul McCartney

I Am A Man Of Constant Sorrow
(from "O Brother, Where Art Thou?")

Words & Music by Carter Stanley

I Fall To Pieces
(from "Coal Miner's Daughter")

Words & Music by Hank Cochran & Harlan Howard

You want me to act like we've nev - er kissed._____ You
You tell me to find some - one else to love._____ Some -

want me to for - get, pre-tend we've nev - er met._____ And I've tried_____ and I've
-one who'll love me too the way you used to do._____ But each time_____ I go

tried, but I have - n't yet_____ you walk by and I fall to
out with some - one new_____ you walk by and I fall to

1
piec - es._____

2
piec - es._____

rall.

195

I Wanna Be Loved By You
(from "Some Like It Hot")

Words by Bert Kalmer
Music by Herbert Stothart & Harry Ruby

I'm not one of the greed-y kind, All of my wants are

sim - ple; I know what's on my mind,

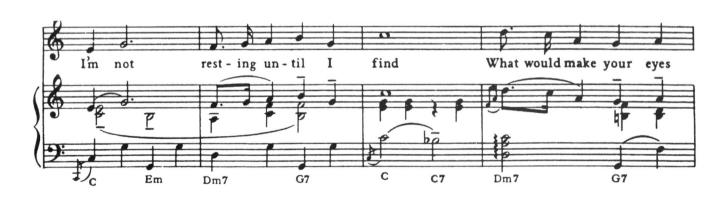

I'm not rest - ing un - til I find What would make your eyes

I Will Survive

(from "The Adventures Of Priscilla Queen Of The Desert")

Words & Music by Dino Fekaris & Freddie Perren

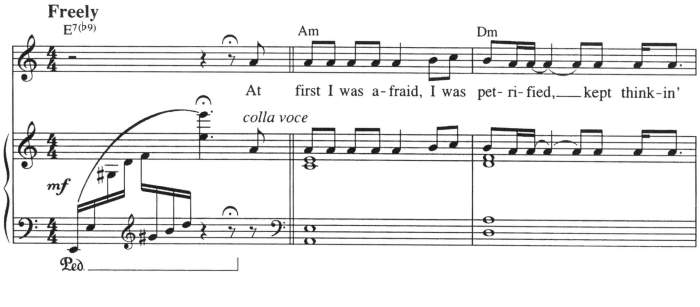

At first I was a-fraid, I was pet- ri-fied,___ kept think-in'

I could nev-er live__with-out you by my side; but then I spent so ma-ny nights__ think-in'

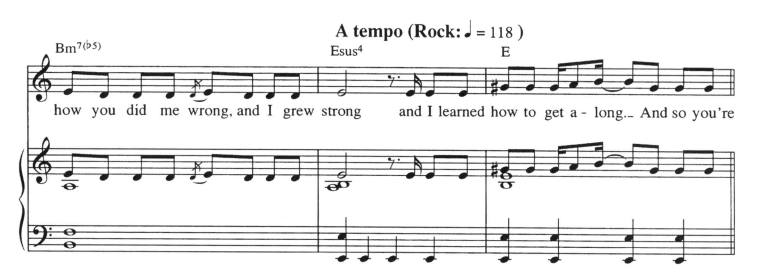

how you did me wrong, and I grew strong and I learned how to get a - long.__ And so you're

I will sur-vive.___ Hey, hey!___

2. It took all the strength_ I had_ not to

fall a - part,___ kept try - in' hard to mend_ the piec - es of my bro-

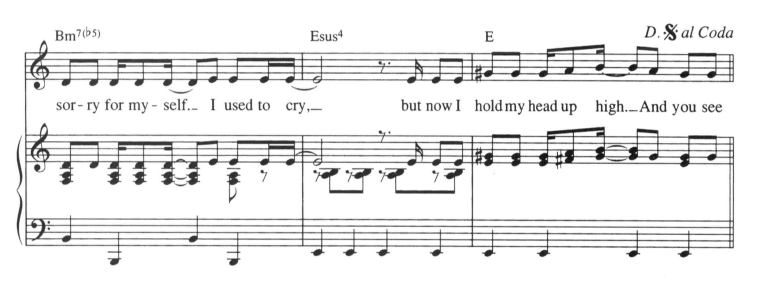

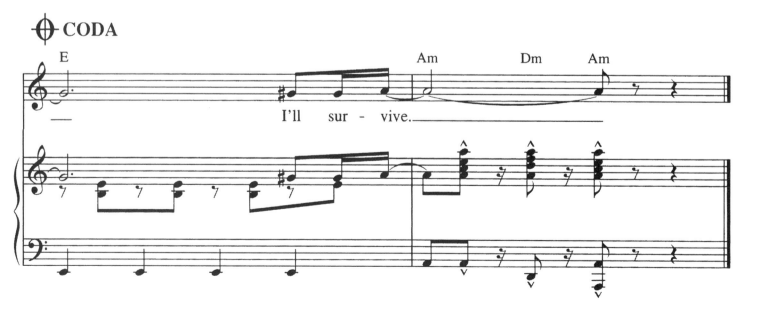

I Will Always Love You
(from "The Bodyguard")

Words & Music by Dolly Parton

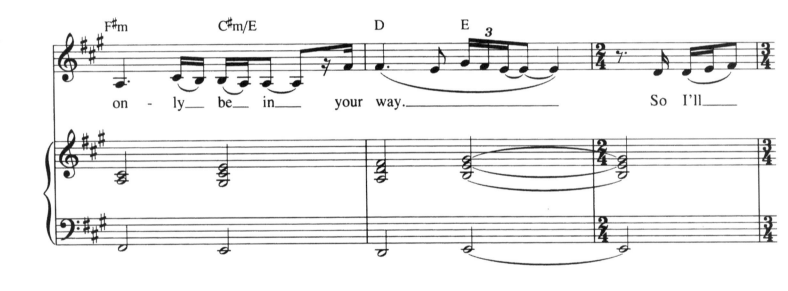

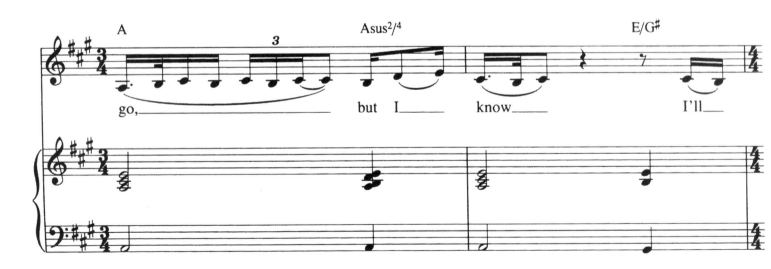

think of you__ ev-'ry step__ of the way.__

a tempo (♩ = 60)

And I_____ will al - ways

love you,_____ I__ will__ al - ways

poco accel.

love you,_____ you,_____ my

205

209

It Could Happen To You
(from "And The Angels Sing")

Words by Johnny Burke
Music by Jimmy Van Heusen

(I've Had) The Time Of My Life

(from "Dirty Dancing")

Words & Music by Frankie Previte, John DeNicola & Donald Markowitz

(M) 1. I've been wait-ing for so long,__ now I've fi-nal-ly found some-one to stand by

me.   (F) We saw the writ-ing on the wall__ as we
        (F) bo - dy and soul__ I want you

felt this ma-gi - cal__ fan-ta - sy.__   (BOTH) Now with
more than you'll ev - er know.__   (M) So we'll

(2° lower harmonies only)

Into The West
(from "The Lord Of The Rings: The Return Of The King")

Words & Music by Annie Lennox, Howard Shore & Fran Walsh

1. Lay down your sweet and wea-ry head.

2. Hope fades in-to the world of night,

through sha-dows fall-ing

Night is fall-ing,

Isn't It Romantic
(from "Love Me Tonight")

Words by Lorenz Hart
Music by Richard Rodgers

Kiss From A Rose
(from "Batman Forever")

Words & Music by Seal

- by,_____ I com-pare you to a kiss from a rose on the

grey,_____ the more I get of you the stran-ger it feels, yeah_____

_____ and now that your rose is in bloom,_____ a

light hits the gloom_ on the grey._____ Ba ya ya ba da ba da da

Vocal tacet 2°

da ba ya ya, ba ya ya ba da ba da da da ba ya ya.

2. There is so much a man can tell you, so much he can

say, you re-main my po-wer, my plea-sure, my pain. Ba-by, to

me you're like a grow-ing ad-dic-tion that I can't de-ny. Won't you tell me, is that

kissed by a rose on the grey.

I've____ been kissed by a rose on the

grey.

I've____ been kissed by a rose on the grey. There is so much a man can

tell you, so much he can say.— You re-main my po-wer, my plea-sure my

pain. To me you're like a growing ad-dic-tion that I can't de-

236

Jailhouse Rock

(from "Jailhouse Rock")

Words & Music by Jerry Leiber & Mike Stoller

Verse 4:

The sad sack was a-sittin' on a block of stone,
Way over in the corner weepin' all alone.
The warden said, "Hey buddy, don't you be no square,
If you can't find a partner use a wooden chair!"
Let's rock *etc.*

Verse 5:

Shifty Henry said to Bugs, "For Heaven's sake,
No one's a lookin', now's our chance to make a break."
Bugsy turned to Shifty and he said, "Nix, nix,
I wanna stick around a while and get my kicks,"
Let's rock, *etc,*

Let The River Run
(from "Working Girl")

Words & Music by Carly Simon

We're com-ing to the edge, run - ning on the wa - ter com-ing through the fog, your sons and daugh ters.

Let the riv-er run, let all the dream - ers wake the

na - tion. Come,_____ the new Je - ru - sa -

trem - bling, sha - ak - ing.___ Oh_____ my heart is

ach - ing. We're com - ing to the edge, run - ning on the wa - ter,

com - ing through the fog, your sons and daugh - ters. We._____ the great and

(D.S.) *Instrumental solo*

small,_____ stand on a star and blaze a trail_____ of de -

244

Live And Let Die
(from "Live And Let Die")

Words & Music by Paul McCartney & Linda McCartney

do it well,— you got - ta give the oth - er fel - low hell!_____

Knockin' On Heaven's Door
(from "Pat Garrett & Billy The Kid")

Words & Music by Bob Dylan

Knock, knock, knock-in' on hea-ven's door___

Knock, knock, knock-in' on hea-ven's door.___

Repeat and fade

Love Is All Around
(from "Four Weddings And A Funeral")

Words & Music by Reg Presley

and so the feel-ing grows.— It's

writ-ten on the wind, it's ev-'ry-where I go,—

so if you real-ly love me, come on and let it show.—

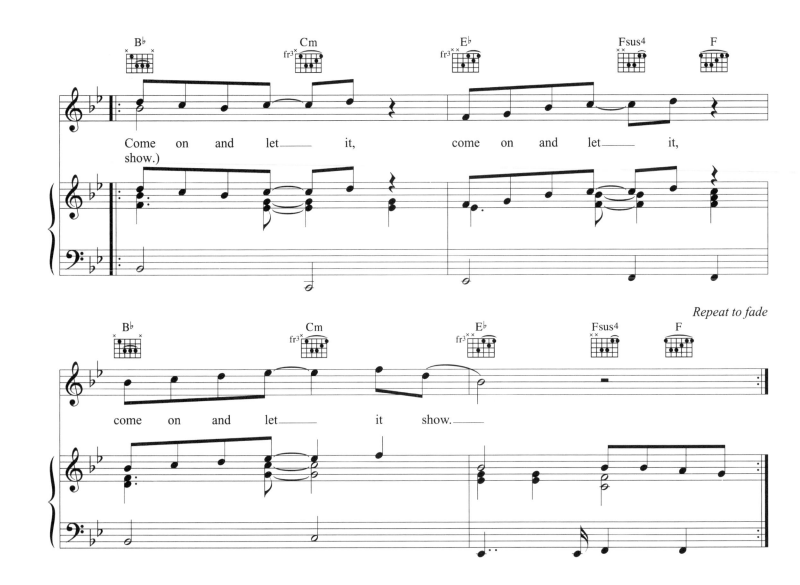

Repeat to fade

Come on and let——— it,
come on and let——— it,
show.)

come on and let——— it show.———

Verse 2:
I see your face before me
As I lay on my bed;
I cannot get to thinking
Of all the things you said.
You gave your promise to me
And I gave mine to you;
I need someone beside me
In everything I do.

Luck Be A Lady
(from "Guys And Dolls")

Words & Music by Frank Loesser

Luck if you've ev - er been a la - dy to be -
-gin with, luck be a la - dy to - night.
Luck let a gen - tle - man see,

how nice a dame you can be,_____

I know the way you've treat - ed oth - er guys you've

been with, luck be a la - dy with me.___

1. A
2. A

260

Long Ago And Far Away
(from "Cover Girl")

Words by Ira Gershwin
Music by Jerome Kern

skies were ov - er - cast, but now the clouds have

passed: you're here at last! _____

Chills run up and down my

spine, A - lad - din's lamp is mine, the

265

266

Mad World
(from "Donnie Darko")

Words & Music by Roland Orzabal

Cello 2° only till *

Meet Me In St. Louis, Louis

(from "Meet Me In St. Louis")

Words & Music by Hugh Martin & Ralph Blane

Meet me in St. Lou - is, Lou - is, meet me

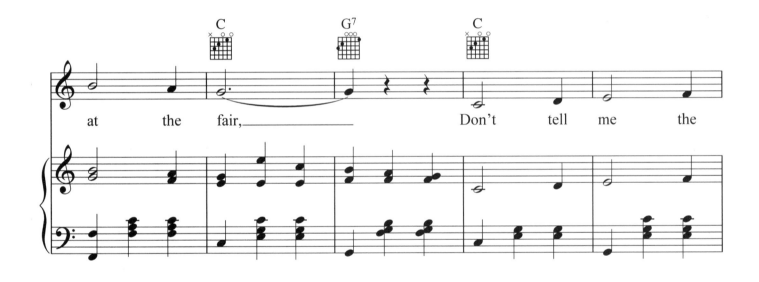

at the fair, _____ Don't tell me the

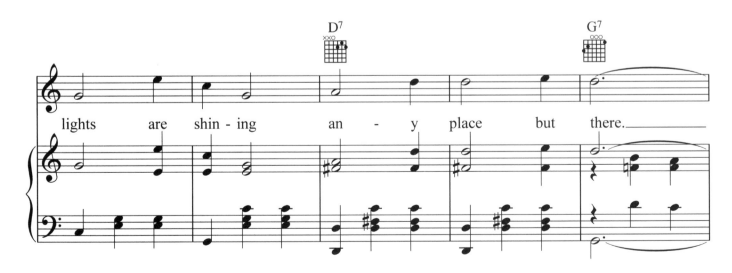

lights are shin - ing an - y place but there. _____

Mrs. Robinson
(from "The Graduate")

Words & Music by Paul Simon

- til you feel at home.___ And here's to you___ Where have you gone

Verse 2:
Hide it in a hiding place
Where no one ever goes
Put it in your pantry
With your cup cakes
It's a little secret
Just the Robinsons affair
Most of all you've got to hide it from the kids.

Koo koo kachoo Mrs. Robinson etc.

Verse 3:
Sitting on a sofa
On a Sunday afternoon
Going to the candidates debate
Laugh about it
Shout about it when you've got to choose
Every way you look at this you lose.

Where have you gone Joe Di Maggio
A nation turns it's lonely eyes to you
Ooh ooh ooh
What's that you say Mrs. Robinson
Jolting Joe has left and gone away
Hey hey hey

My Favourite Things
(from "The Sound Of Music")

Words by Oscar Hammerstein II
Music by Richard Rodgers

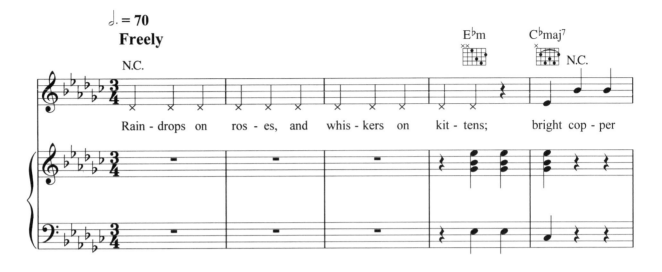

Rain - drops on ros - es, and whis - kers on kit - tens; bright cop - per

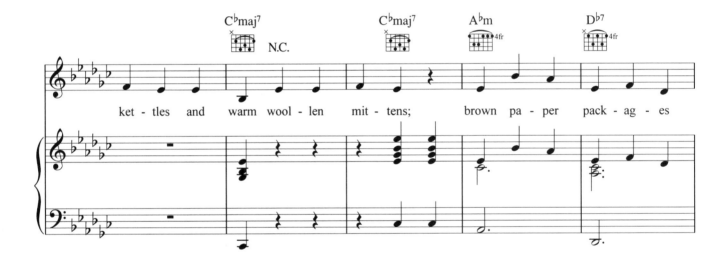

ket - tles and warm wool - len mit - tens; brown pa - per pack - ag - es

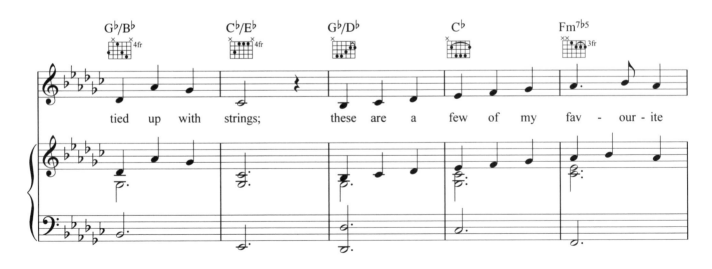

tied up with strings; these are a few of my fav - our - ite

things.

Cream col - oured pon - ies and crisp ap - ple stru - dels;

door - bells and sleigh - bells and schnitz - el with nood - les; wild geese that

fly with the moon on their wings; these are a few of my

My Heart Will Go On
(from "Titanic")

Words by Will Jennings
Music by James Horner

1. Ev - 'ry night in my dreams I see you, I
2. Love can touch us one time and last for a

Con pedale

You're here, there's no - thing I fear

and I know that my heart will go

on. We'll

stay for - ev - er this way. You are

Moon River
(from "Breakfast At Tiffany's")

Words by Johnny Mercer
Music by Henry Mancini

heart - - break - er, wher - ev - er you're go - in',____ I'm

go - in'____ your way. Two drift - ers,

off to see the world. There's such a lot of

world to see._____ We're af - -

293

Nine To Five
(from "Nine To Five")

Words & Music by Dolly Parton

Original Key: F♯ major

♩ = 100

get - ting by,_____ it's all tak - ing and_ no giv - ing. They just

use_ your mind and they nev - er give_ you cred - it. It's e -

-nough to drive_ you cra - zy if_ you let_ it._____

Nine to_ five_ for ser - vice and_ de - vo - tion you would

297

think___ that I_____ would de - serve a fair___ pro - mo - tion. Want to

move___ a - head___ but the boss___ won't seem to let___ me. I

swear some - times___ that man is out___ to get___ me.

D.S. al Coda

2.They

Oh, Pretty Woman

(from "Oh, Pretty Woman")

Words & Music by Roy Orbison & Bill Dees

wo - man, walk - ing down the street, pret - ty wo - man, the kind I

wo - man, won't you par - don me,___ pret - ty wo - man, I could-n't

wo - man, don't walk on by,___ pret - ty wo - man, don't

like to meet,___ pret - ty wo - man, I don't be -
help but see,___ pret - ty wo - man, that you look
make me cry,___ pret - ty wo - man, don't walk a -

lieve___ you, you're not the truth, no one can look as good as you.
love - ly as can be.___ Are you lone - ly just like me?
way,___

Come with me ba - by,____ be mine to -

night._____

D.S. al Coda

3. Pret - ty

CODA

hey, O. K.___

if that's the way it must be O. K.

303

I guess I'll go on home___ it's late,___ There'll be to-

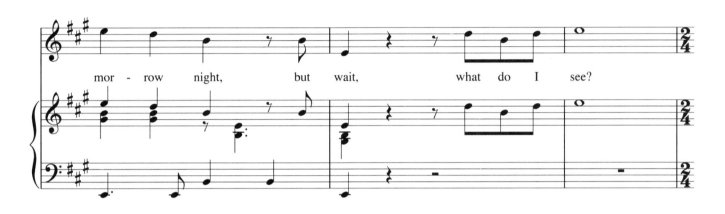

mor - row night, but wait, what do I see?

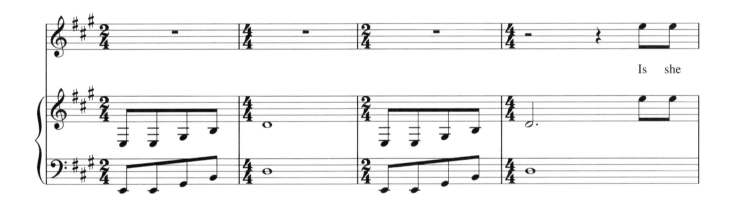

Is she

walk - ing back to me.___

Yeah,   she's walk - ing back   to   me.___

Oh,_____   pret - ty wo - man.

Ol' Man River

(from "Show Boat")

Words by Oscar Hamerstein II
Music by Jerome Kern

Col-oured folks work on de Mis - sis - sip - pi, col-oured folks work while de

white folks play. Pull-in' dose boats from de dawn to sun - set,

sick of try-in', Ah'm tired of liv-in' an' skeered of dy-in', but

ol' man riv-er, he jus' keeps roll-in' a - long.

long.

Old Time Rock And Roll

(from "Risky Business")

Words & Music by George Jackson & Thomas Jones III

313

Won't go to hear 'em play a   Still like that old____ time a

rock and   roll____   that kind of mu - sic just   soothes the soul.____
(2° a capella)

D7

I rem - i - nisce a - bout the days of old_____ with that old_____ time a

G7   **D7**

Repeat and fade

rock and roll._____ Still like that old_____ time a

3.   (Won't go to hear 'em play a) tango
       I'd rather hear some blues or funky soul.
       There's only one sure way to get me to go
       Start playing old time rock and roll.

4.   Call me a relic, call me what you will
       Say I'm old-fashioned, say I'm over the hill
       Today's music ain't got the same soul
       I like that old time rock and roll.

       (to chorus)

Peaches
(from "Sexy Beast")

Words & Music by Jean-Jacques Burnel, Jet Black, Hugh Cornwell & David Greenfield

1. Stroll- ing a - long mind- ing my own busi - ness.
(Verse 2 (𝄊) see block lyric)

Well there goes a girl and a half, she's got me go- in'.

Up and down,— she's got me go- in' up and down.—

Lap me up,—— why don't you come on and lap me up.——

Walk-ing on the beach-es look - ing at the peach-es.

Well there goes an-oth-er one just ly - ing down on the sand dunes. I'd

bet-ter go take a swim   and see if I can cool down— a lit-tle bit.—

'Cos you and me, wo-man,   we got-ta lot-ta

things on our minds.—   (You know what I mean.)

D.%. al Coda

Walk-ing on the beach-es look - ing at the peach-es.

Just look at all the peaches   down on the beaches.   Mm mm mm

mm mm mm mm mm.   Mm mm mm   mm mm mm mm mm.

Mm.—   Mm.—   Mm mm mm

mm mm mm mm mm.

Verse 2:
Well you just take a look over there
(Where? There)
Is she trying to get out of that clitoris?
Liberation for women
That's what I preach
(Preacher man)
Walking on the beaches
Looking at the peaches.

Oh shit there goes the charabang
Looks like I'm gonna be stuck here
The whole summer
Well what a bummer.

Pinball Wizard
(from "Tommy")

Words & Music by Pete Townshend

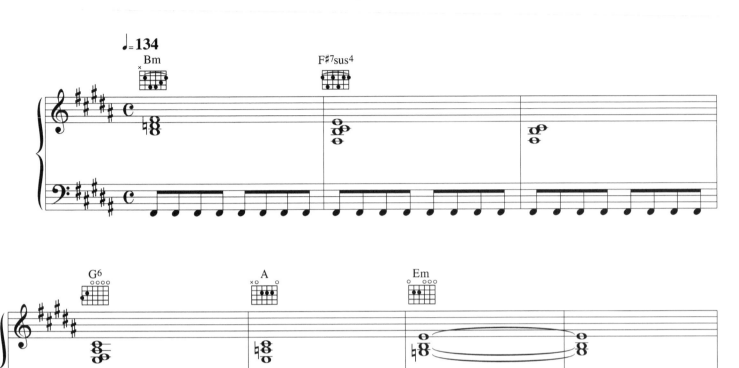

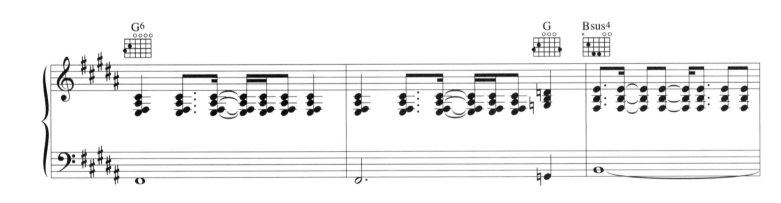

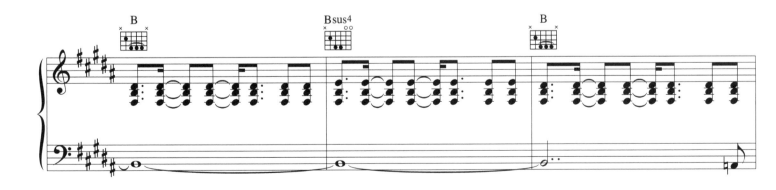

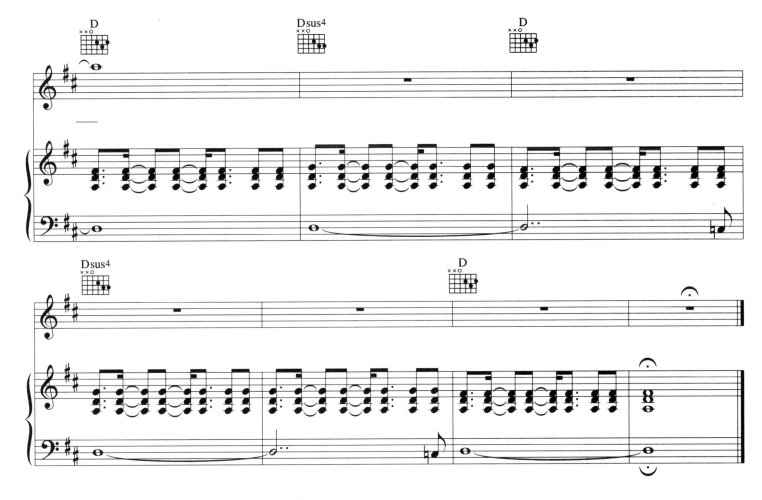

Verse 2:
He stands like a statue
Becomes part of the machine.
Feeling all the bumpers
Always playing clean.
He plays by intuition
The digit counters fall.
That deaf, dumb and blind kid
Sure plays a mean pinball.

Verse 3:
He's got no distractions
Can't hear those buzzers and bells.
Don't see no lights a' flashin'
He plays by sense of smell.
Always gets a replay
And never tilts at all.
That deaf, dumb and blind kid
Sure plays a mean pinball.

I thought I was
The Bally table king
But I just handed
My pinball crown to him.
How do you think he does it?
(I don't know)
What makes him so good?

Verse 4:
Even at my favourite table
He can beat my best
The kids all lead him in
And he just does the rest.
He's got crazy flipper fingers
Never seen him fall.
That deaf, dumb and blind kid
Sure plays a mean pinball.

Pure Shores
(from "The Beach")

Words & Music by Shaznay Lewis & William Orbit

1. I've crossed des - erts for miles,___ swam wa - ter for a time,___
(Verse 2 see block lyric)

Ooh.

Mov - in', ___ com - in', ___ can you hear what I ___ hear (hear ___ it out ___ of reach.) I hear ___ it call -

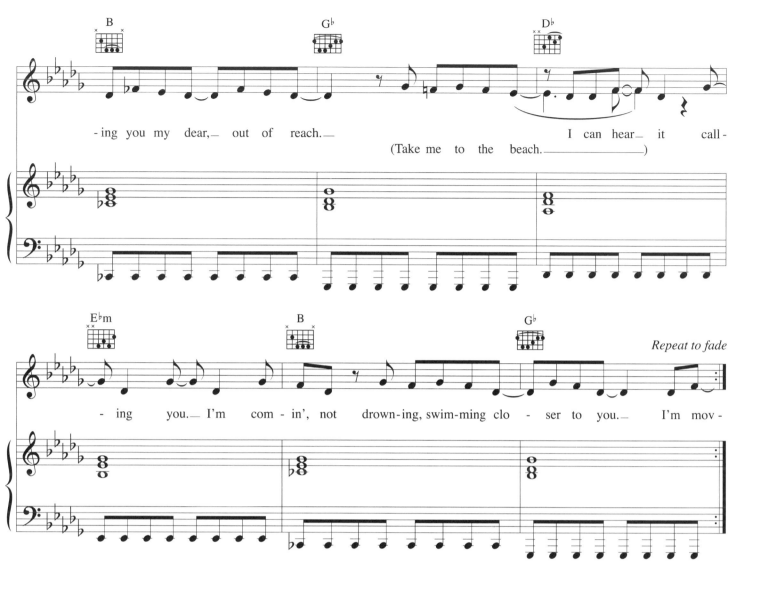

Verse 2:
Never been here before
I'm intrigued, I'm unsure
I'm searching for more
I've got something that's all mine
I've got something that's all mine.

Take me somewhere I can breathe
I've got so much to see
This is where I wanna be
In a place I can call mine
In a place I can call mine.

I'm movin' *etc*.

Purple Rain

(from "Purple Rain")

Words & Music by Prince

Raindrops Keep Falling On My Head

(from "Butch Cassidy And The Sundance Kid")

Words by Hal David
Music by Burt Bacharach

Rock Around The Clock
(from "Blackboard Jungle")
Words & Music by Max C. Freedman & Jimmy De Knight

One, two, three o'-clock, four o'-clock rock, five, six, sev-en o'-clock, eight o' clock rock.

Nine, ten, e-le-ven o'-clock, twelve o' clock rock, we're gon-na rock a-round the clock to-night. Put your

glad rags on and join me, Hon,_ we'll have some fun when the clock strikes one,_ we're gon-na

(Verse 2-5 see block lyric)

Verse 2:
When the clock strikes two and three and four
If the band slows down we'll yell for more.
We're gonna rock around the clock tonight
We're gonna rock, rock, rock 'til broad daylight
We're gonna rock, gonna rock around the clock tonight.

Verse 3:
When the chimes ring five and six and seven
We'll be rockin' up in seventh heav'n.
We're gonna rock around the clock tonight
We're gonna rock, rock, rock 'til broad daylight
We're gonna rock, gonna rock around the clock tonight.

Verse 4:
When it's eight, nine, ten, eleven, too
I'll be goin' strong and so will you.
We're gonna rock around the clock tonight
We're gonna rock, rock, rock 'til broad daylight
We're gonna rock, gonna rock around the clock tonight.

Verse 5:
When the clock strikes twelve, we'll cool off, then
Start a rockin' 'round the clock again.
We're gonna rock around the clock tonight
We're gonna rock, rock, rock 'til broad daylight
We're gonna rock, gonna rock around the clock tonight.

Put The Blame On Mame
(from "Gilda")

Words & Music by Allan Roberts & Doris Fisher

Sea Of Love
(from "Sea Of Love")

Words & Music by George Khoury & Philip Bastiste

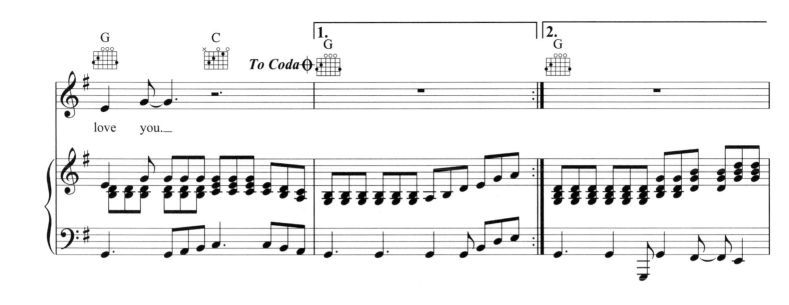

love you.___

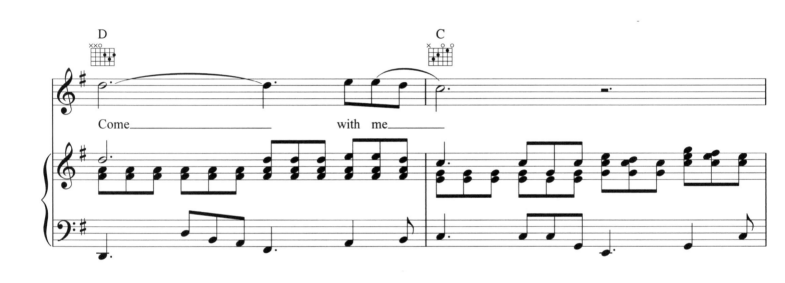

Come_____ with me_____

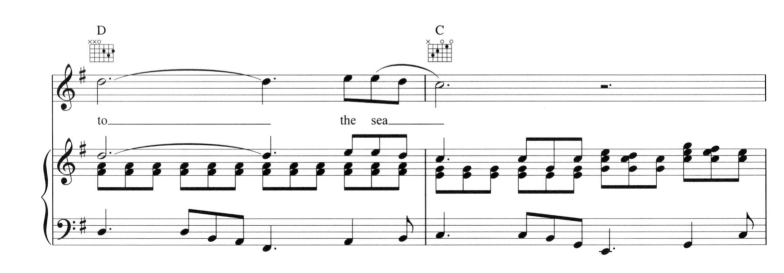

to_____ the sea_____

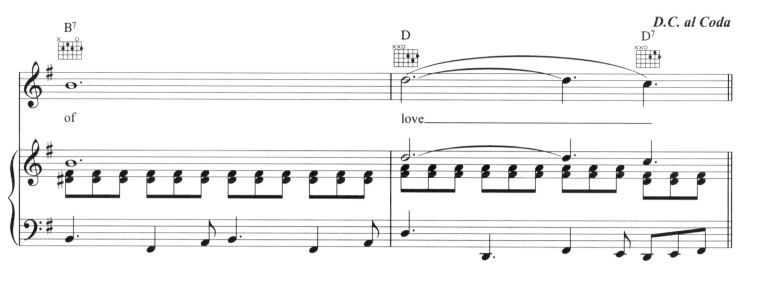

of   love

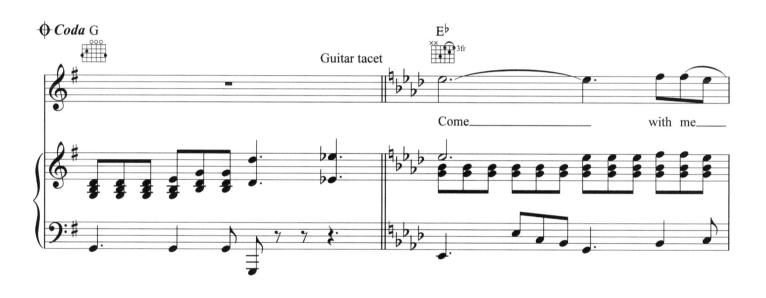

Come   with me

to   the sea

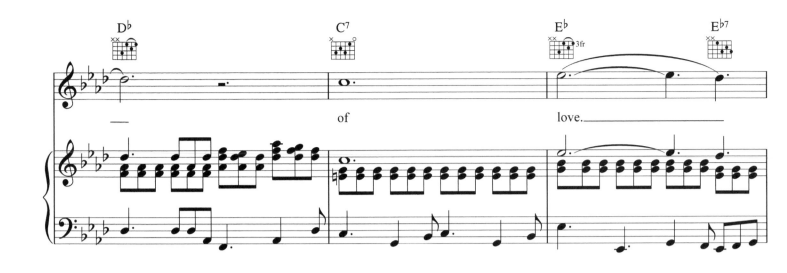

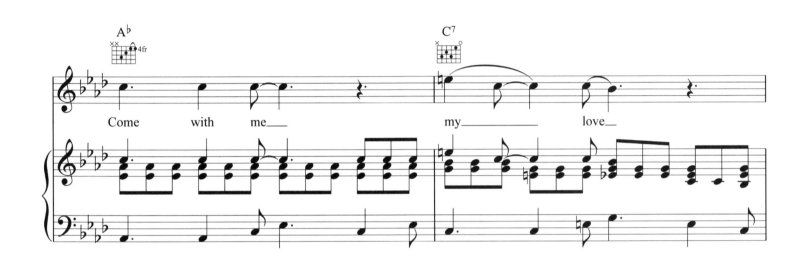

I____ want to tell you just how__ much I love you.__

I_____ want to tell you,

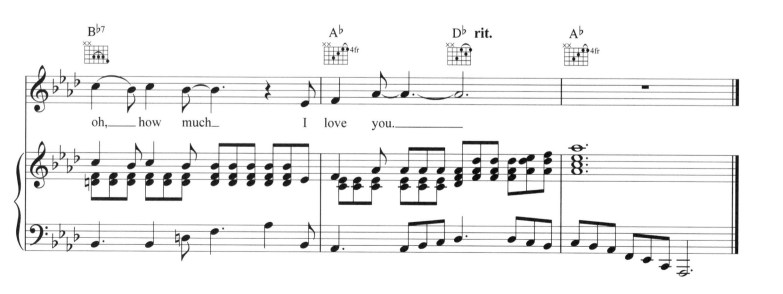

oh,___ how much__ I love you._____

Shall We Dance

(from "The King And I")

Words by Oscar Hammerstein II
Music by Richard Rodgers

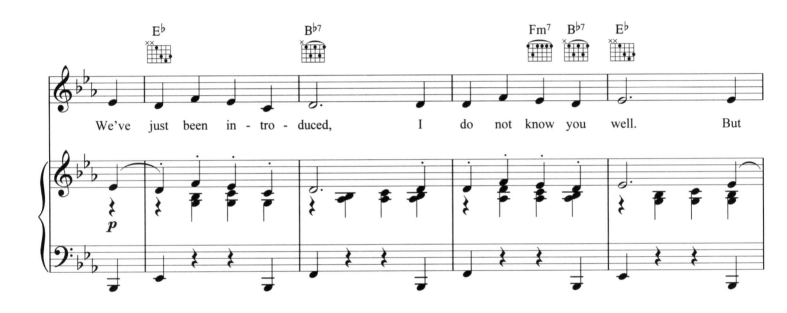

We've just been in-tro-duced, I do not know you well. But

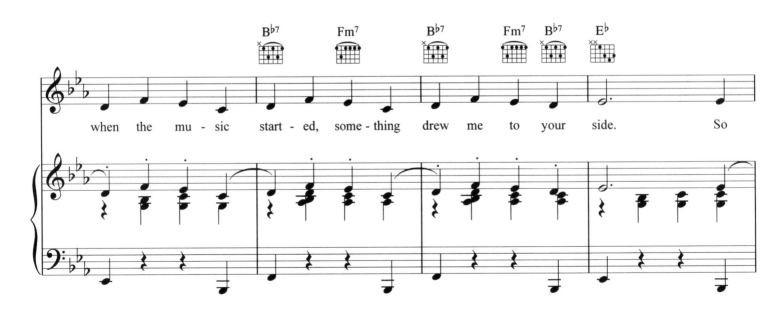

when the mu-sic start-ed, some-thing drew me to your side. So

Shall we then say "Good-night" and mean "good-bye?" Or, per-chance_____ when the last lit-tle star has left the sky. Shall we still be to-geth-er with our arms a-round each

oth - er, And shall you be my new ro - mance?____

— On the clear un - der - stand - ing that this

kind of thing can hap - pen, Shall we dance? Shall we dance? Shall we

1. dance? Shall we **2.** dance?____

She
(from "Notting Hill")

Words by Herbert Kretzmer
Music by Charles Aznavour

sing, ___ may be the chill that au - tumn brings, ___ may be a hun - dred diff - 'rent

things ___ with - in the mea - sure of a day.

2. She ___ may be the beau - ty or the beast, ___ may be the fa - mine or the
(Verse 3 instr. Verse 4 see block lyric)

feast, ___ may turn each day in - to a hea - ven or ___ hell.

363

She— may be the love that can-not hope to last,— may come to me from sha - dows of the past— that I'll re-mem - ber till the day I die.

Coda

She, she,_____ she.

Verse 4:
She may be the reason I survive
The why and wherefore I'm alive
The one I'll care for through the rough and ready years.
Me, I'll take her laughter and her tears
And make them all my souvenirs
For where she goes I've got to be
The meaning of my life is she, she, she.

Sisters Of Mercy
(from "McCabe & Mrs. Miller")

Words & Music by Leonard Cohen

Coda

We weren't lov- ers like that, And be-sides, it would still be all right.____

ritard.

Additional Lyrics

2. Yes, you who must leave everything
   That you cannot control,
   It begins with your family,
   But soon it comes round to your soul.
   Well, I've been where you're hanging,
   I think I can see how you're pinned.
   When you're not feeling holy,
   Your loneliness says that you've sinned.

3. They lay down beside me,
   I made my confession to them.
   They touched both my eyes,
   And I touched the dew on their hem.
   If your life is a leaf
   That the seasons tear off and condemn,
   They will bind you with love
   That is graceful and green as a stem.

4. When I left, they were sleeping,
   I hope you run into them soon.
   Don't turn on the lights,
   You can read their address by the moon.
   And you won't make me jealous
   If I hear that they sweetened your night.
   We weren't lovers like that,
   And besides, it would still be all right.
   We weren't lovers like that,
   And besides, it would still be all right.

Some Day My Prince Will Come

(from "Snow White And The Seven Dwarfs")

Words by Larry Morey
Music by Frank Churchill

Spooky
(from "Lock, Stock And Two Smoking Barrels")

Words & Music by Harry Middlebrooks & Mike Shapiro

1. In the cool of the eve-nin' when ev - 'ry-thing is get-tin' kind of

(Verses 2 & 3 see block lyrics)

groo - vy,___ you call me up and ask me would I

like to go with you and see a mo - vie.___

First I say no, I've got some plans for to - night___ and then I stop and

say al - right.___ Love___ is kind - a cra - zy with a spoo - ky lit - tle boy like you.

Finger click

1.

To Coda ✪ Em7

2.

2. You spoo - ky.___

Verse 2:

You always keep me guessing
I never seem to know what you are thinking
And if a girl looks at you
It's for sure your little eye will be a-winking
I get confused, I never know where I stand
And then you smile and hold my hand
Love is kinda crazy with a spooky little boy like you.

Verse 3:

If you decide someday
To stop this little game that you are playing
I'm gonna tell you all the things
My heart's been a-dying to be saying
Just like a ghost
You've been a-hauntin' my dreams
But now I know you're not what you seem
Love is kinda crazy with a spooky little boy like you.

Show Me Heaven
(from "Romeo And Juliet")

Words & Music by Maria McKee, Jay Rifkin & Eric Rackin

Verse 2:
Here I go, I'm shaking just like the breeze.
Hey babe, Ineed your hand to steady me.
I'm not denying I'm frightened as much as you.
Though I'm barely touching you,
I've shivers down my spine, and it feels divine.

Oh, show me heaven, *etc.*

Stand By Me
(from "Stand By Me")
Words & Music by Ben E. King, Jerry Leiber & Mike Stoller

Slowly

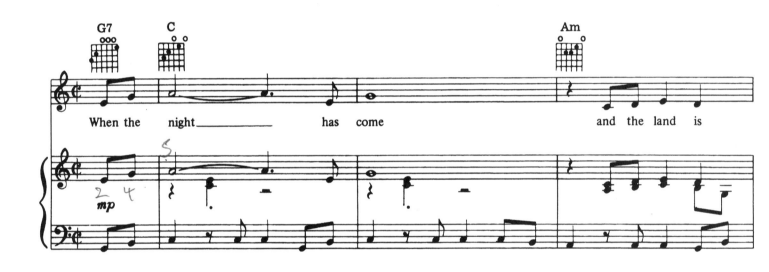

When the night＿＿＿ has come＿＿＿ and the land is

dark And the moon＿＿＿ is the on-ly＿＿＿ light we'll

see,   No, I won't   be a - fraid,   no_____ I

won't   be a - fraid   Just as   long_____ as you

stand,_____ Stand By   Me.   So,   dar - ling,   dar - ling,

Stand ____ By Me, oh, __ Stand ____ By Me, Oh,

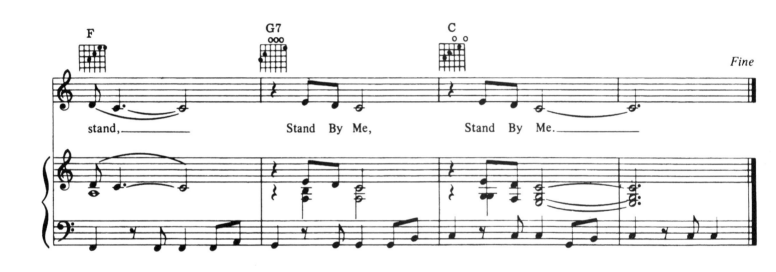

stand, _____ Stand By Me, Stand By Me. _____

Fine

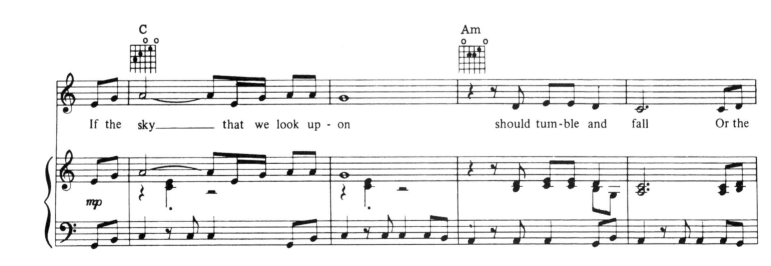

If the sky ____ that we look up - on should tum-ble and fall Or the

moun-tain _____ should crum-ble _____ in the sea, I won't

cry, I won't cry, no _____ I ___ won't shed a tear Just as

D. S. al Fine

long _____ as you stand, _____ Stand By Me. So, dar-ling, dar-ling,

Stayin' Alive
(from "Saturday Night Fever")

Words & Music by Barry Gibb, Maurice Gibb & Robin Gibb

all right._ It's O K.__ And you may look_ the oth - er way._
all right._ It's O K.__ I'll live to see_ an - oth - er day._

We can try_ to un - der - stand_ the New York Times' ef - fect_ on man._

Wheth - er you're a broth-er or wheth - er you're a moth-er, you're stay - in' a-live,_ stay-in' a-live._

Feel the cit- y break-in' and ev - 'ry-bod-y shak-in', and we're stay-in' a-live,_ stay-in' a-live._

Ah, ha, ha, ha, stay-in' a-live,_ stay-in' a-live._ Ah, ha, ha, ha,

stay-in' a-live.____

Well now, I_

Life go-in' no-where.____

Some-bod-y help me.____ Some-bod-y help_ me, yeah.__

Life go-in' no-where.__ Some-bod-y help_ me, yeah._

Stay-in' a-live._____ Well, you can tell__

Life go-in' no-where.__

Repeat and fade

Stormy Weather
(from "Stormy Weather")

Words by Ted Koehler
Music by Harold Arlen

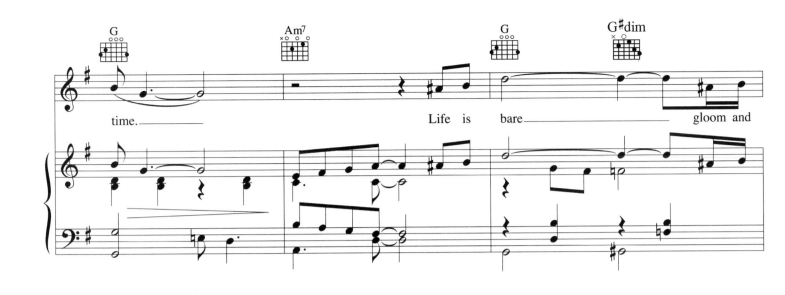

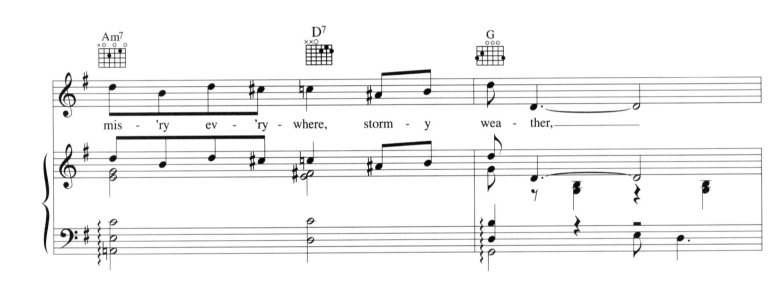

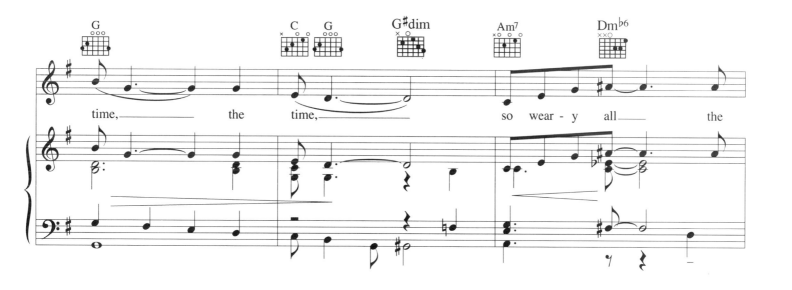

time, _____ the time, _____ so wear-y all _____ the

time. _____ When she went a - way _____ the blues walked

in and met me. If she stays a - way _____ old rock - in'

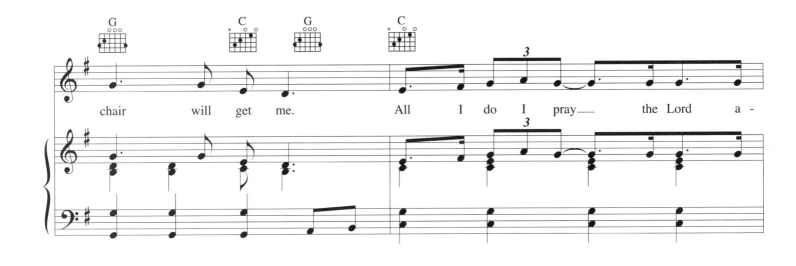

chair will get me. All I do I pray___ the Lord a -

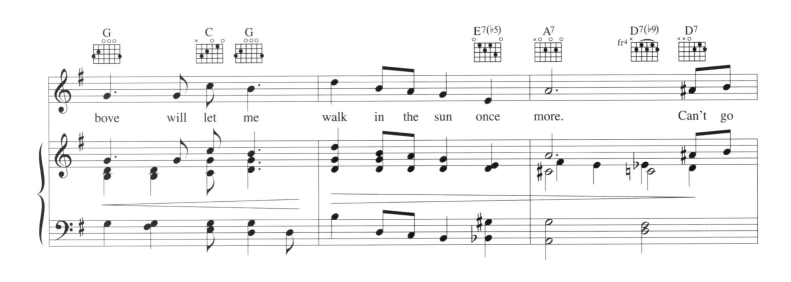

bove will let me walk in the sun once more. Can't go

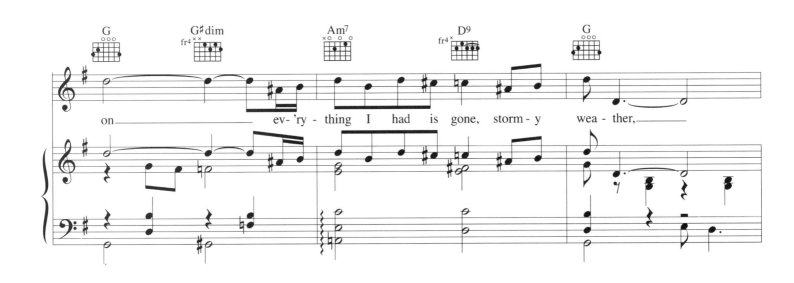

on___ ev-'ry - thing I had is gone, storm - y wea - ther,___

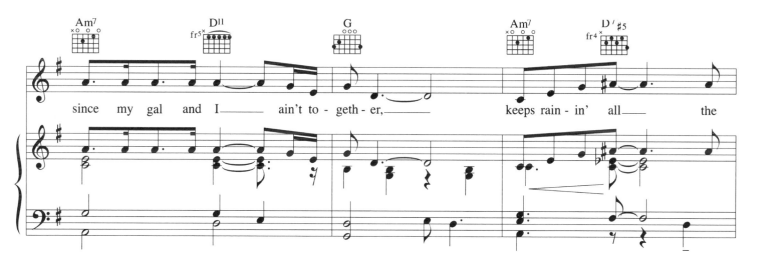

since my gal and I_____ ain't to-geth-er,_____ keeps rain-in' all_____ the

time,_____ keeps rain-in' all_____ the time._____

1.

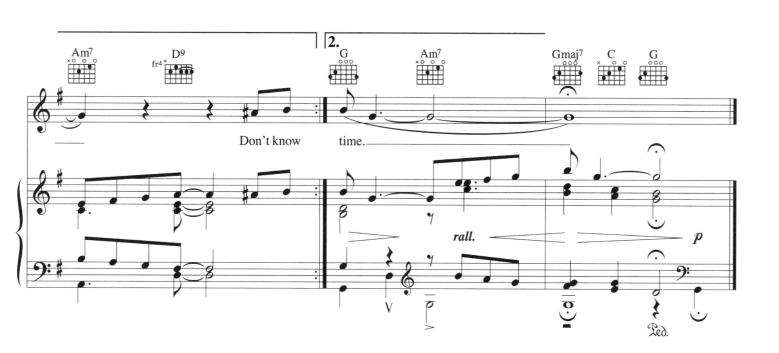

2.

Don't know time._____

rall.

p

393

Stuck In The Middle With You

(from "Resevoir Dogs")

Words & Music by Gerry Rafferty & Joe Egan

Verse 2:

Yes I'm stuck in the middle with you,
And I'm wondering what it is I should do.
It's so hard to keep the smile from my face
Losing control, yeah I'm all over the place.
Clowns to the left of me, jokers to the right,
Here I am, stuck in the middle with you.

Verse 3:

Well I'm trying to make some sense of it all,
I can see that it makes no sense at all.
Is it cool to go to sleep on the floor,
I don't think that I can take any more.
Clowns to the left of me, joker to the right,
Here I am, stuck in the middle with you.

Verse 4: Instrumental

Take My Breath Away
(from "Top Gun")

Words by Tom Whitlock
Music by Giorgio Moroder

-n'lly lov - ers know no shame. _____
be - come the fa - ted ones. _____
where there's a love in flames. _____

Turn - ing and re - turn - ing to _____
Turn - ing and re - turn - ing to _____
Turn - ing and re - turn - ing to _____

_____ some se - cret place in - side; _____
_____ some se - cret place to hide; _____
_____ some se - cret place in - side; _____

watch - ing in slow mo - tion as ____ you turn a - round and
watch - ing in slow mo - tion as ____ you turn my way and
watch - ing in slow mo - tion as ____ you turn to me and

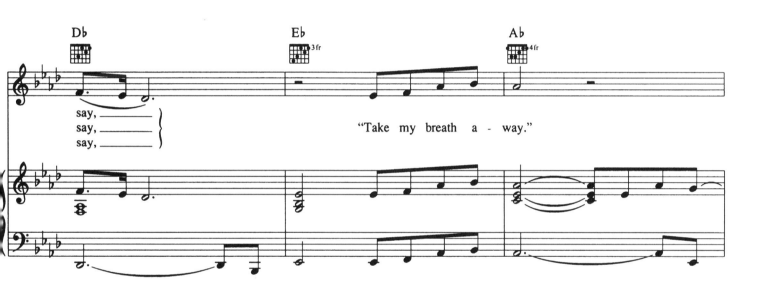

say, ____
say, ____
say, ____

"Take my breath a - way."

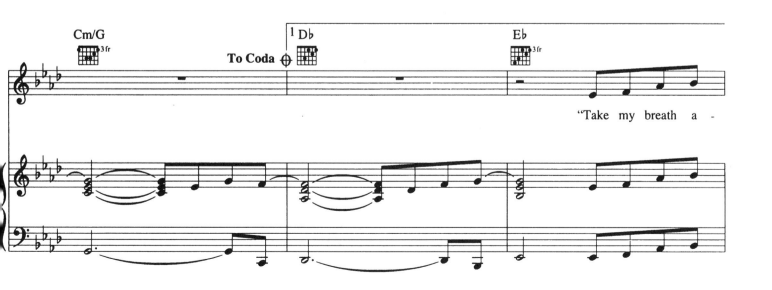

To Coda

"Take my breath a -

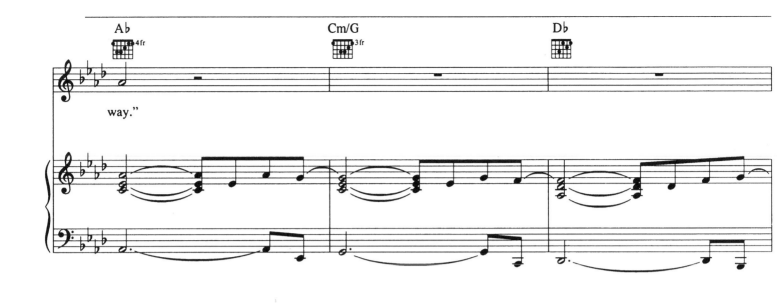

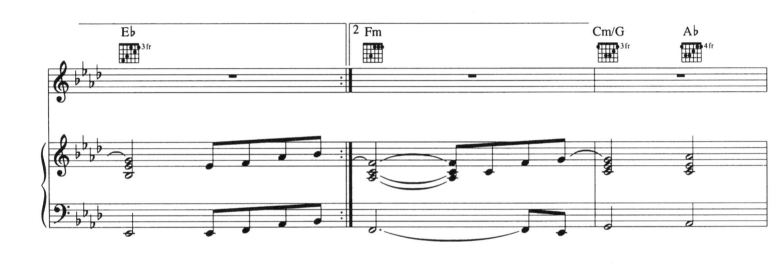

Through the hour - glass I saw ___ you. In time, ___ you slipped _ a - way.

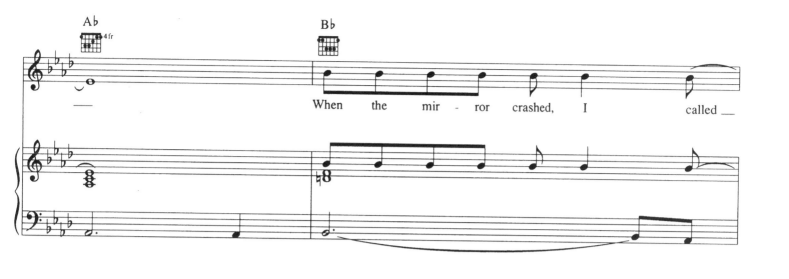

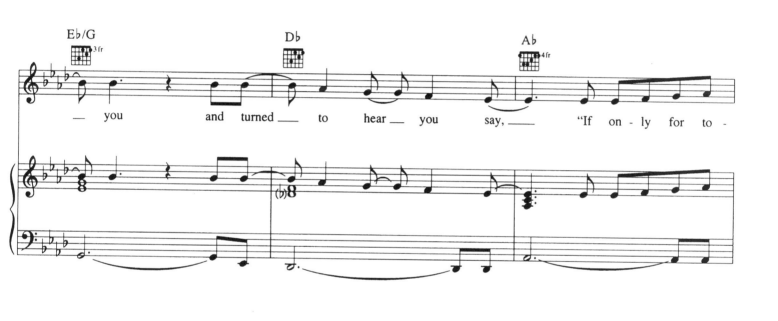

The Trail Of The Lonesome Pine
(from "Way Out West")

Words by Ballard McDonald
Music by Harry Carroll

In the Blue Ridge Moun-tains of Vir-gin-ia, on the trail of the lone-some pine, in the pale moon-shine our hearts en-twine where she carved her name and I carved mine. Oh

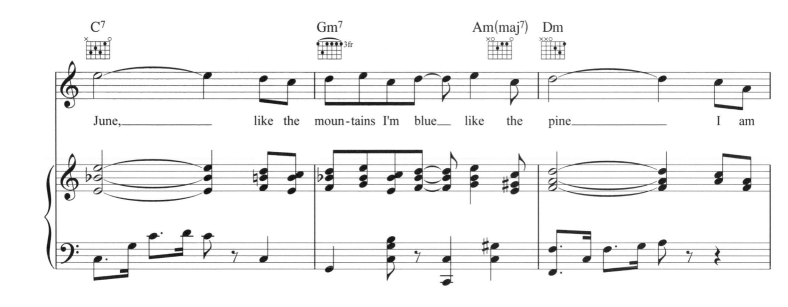

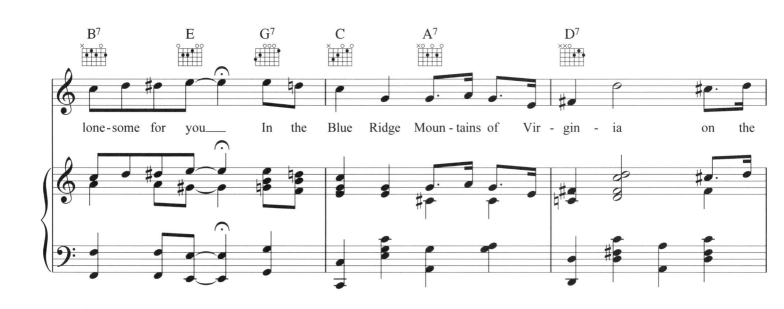

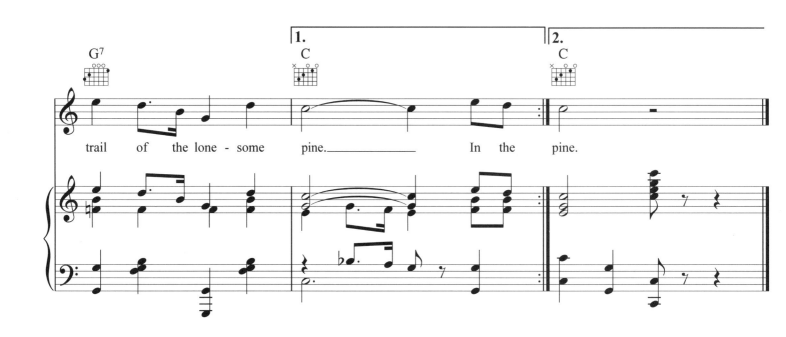

Three Coins In The Fountain

(from "Three Coins In The Fountain")

Words by Sammy Cahn
Music by Jule Styne

Rome. Which one will the foun-tain bless? Which one will the foun-tain

bless? Three coins in the foun-tain, Through the rip-ples how they shine

Just one wish will be grant-ed One heart will wear a val-en-tine. Make it mine! Make it

mine! Make it mine! _____ mine! _____

Try A Little Tenderness
(from "The Commitments")

Words & Music by Harry Woods, Jimmy Campbell & Reg Connelly

She may be wea - ry,___ wo - men do get wea - ry___

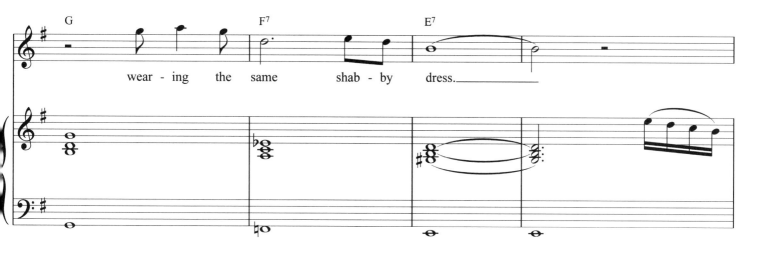

wear - ing the same shab - by dress.___

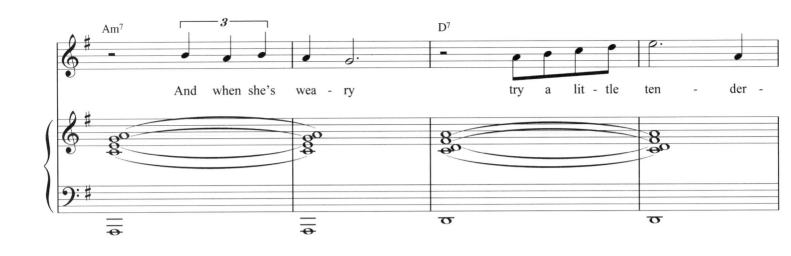

And when she's wea - ry   try a lit - tle ten - der-

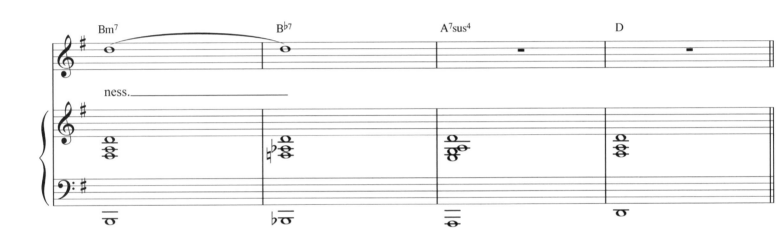

ness._____

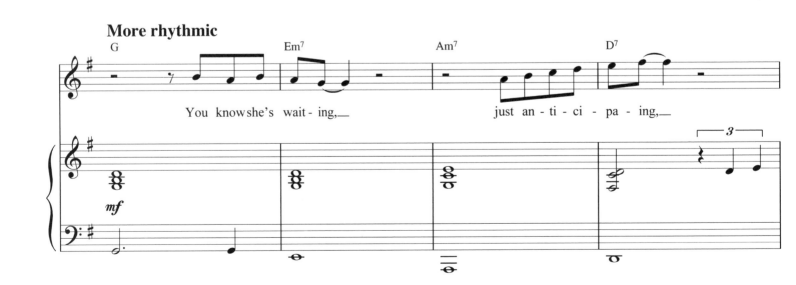

More rhythmic

You know she's wait - ing,___   just an - ti - ci - pa - ing,___

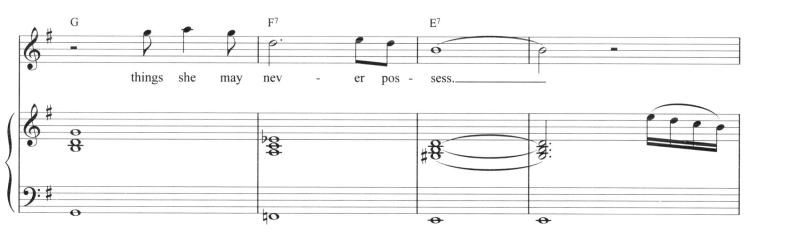

things she may nev - er pos - sess._____

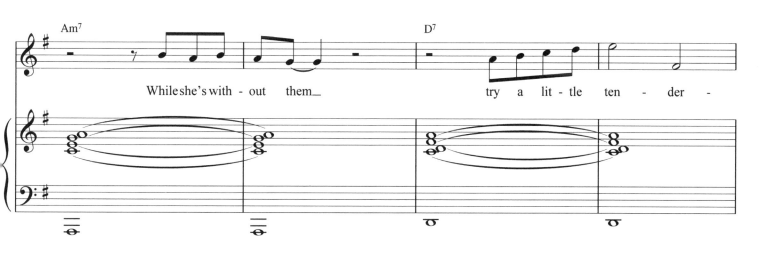

While she's with - out them___ try a lit - tle ten - der -

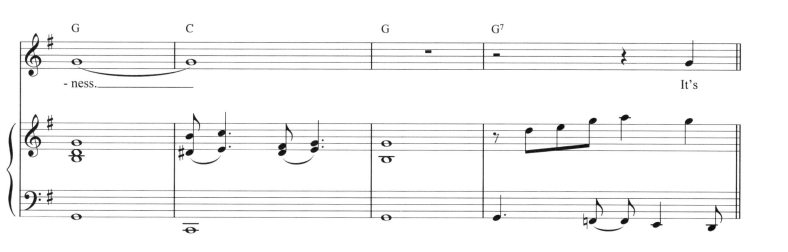

- ness._____ It's

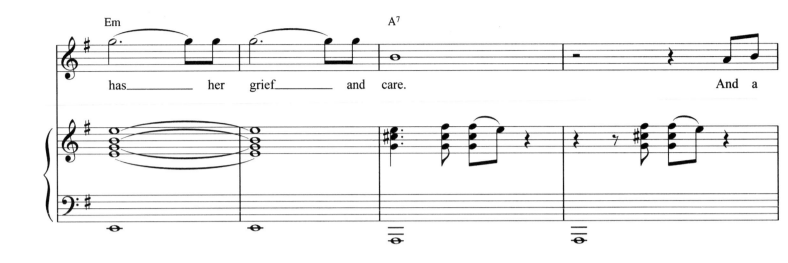

has _____ her grief _____ and care.

And a

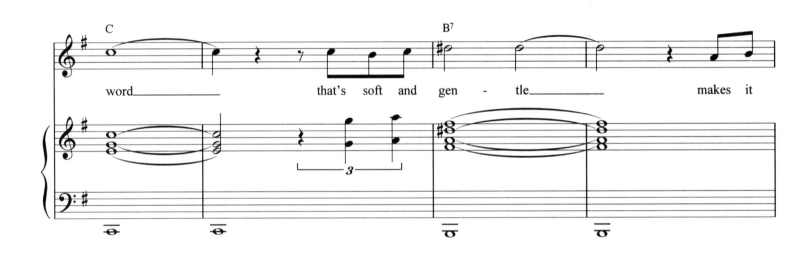

word _____ that's soft and gen - tle _____ makes it

ea - si - er _____ to bear. _____

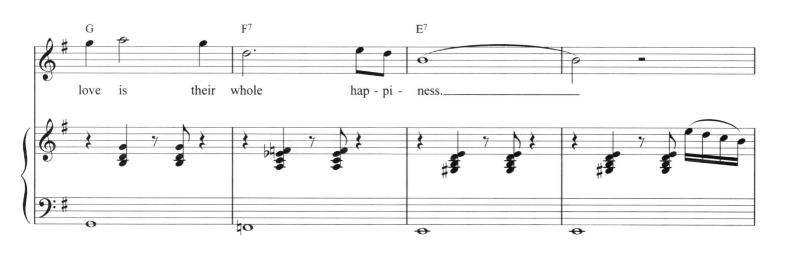

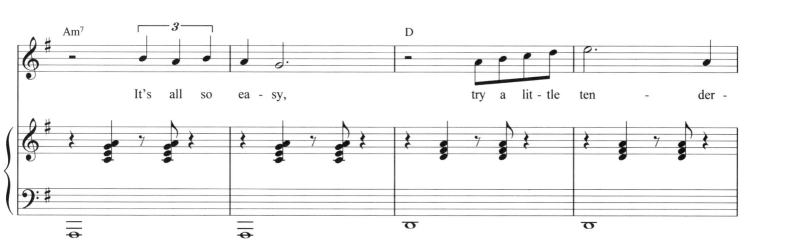

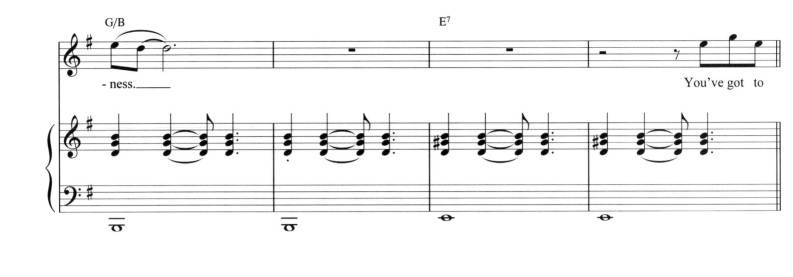

Unchained Melody
(from "Ghost")

Words by Hy Zaret
Music by Alex North

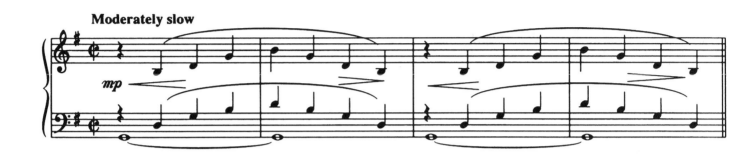

Moderately slow

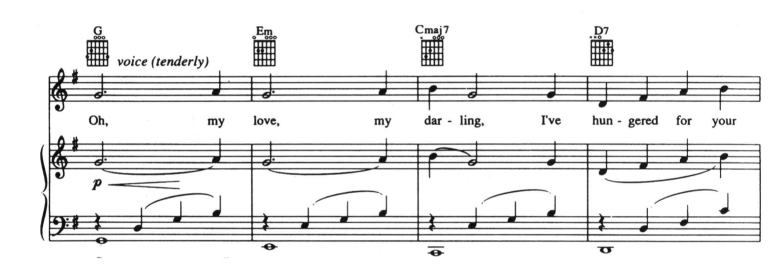

Oh, my love, my dar - ling, I've hun - gered for your

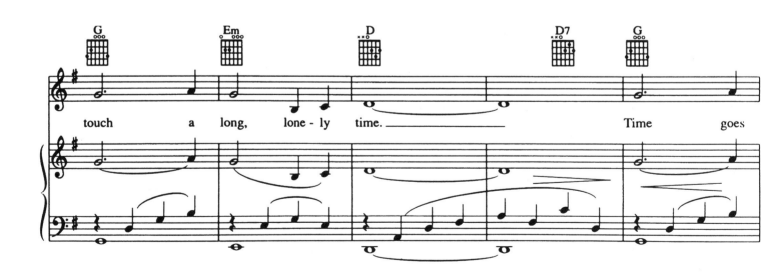

touch a long, lone - ly time. _____ Time goes

by   so   slow-ly   and   time   can   do   so   much,   Are   you   still

mine? _____   I   need   your   love, _____   I   need   your   love, _____

God   speed   your   love _____   to   me! _____

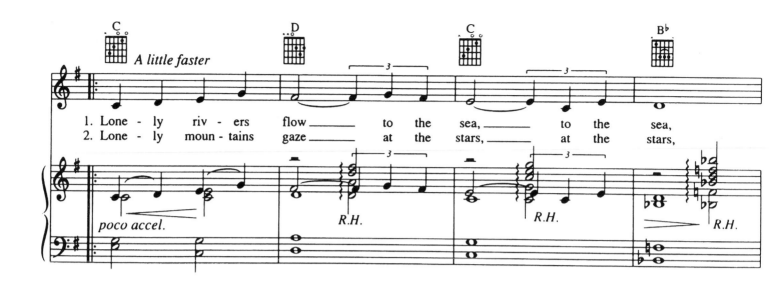

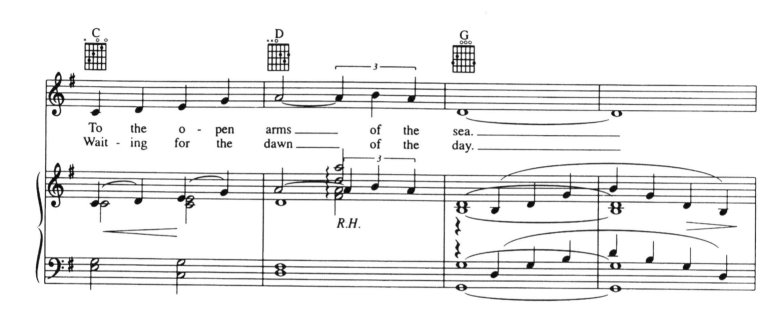

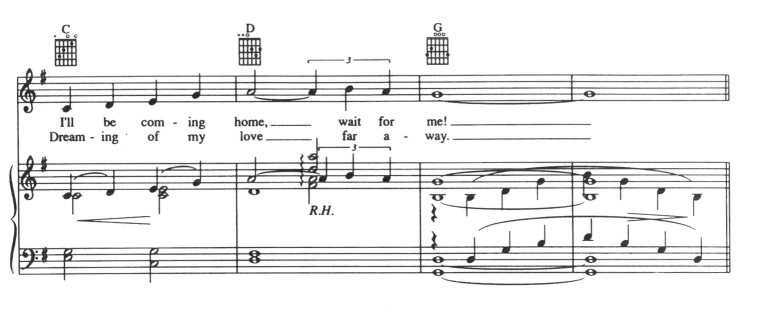

I'll be com - ing home, ___ wait for me! ___
Dream - ing of my love ___ far a - way. ___

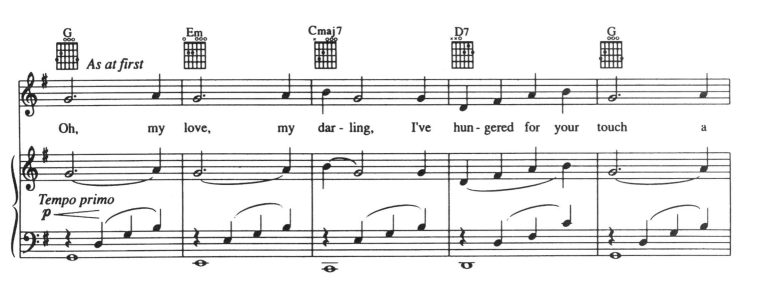

Oh, my love, my dar - ling, I've hun - gered for your touch a

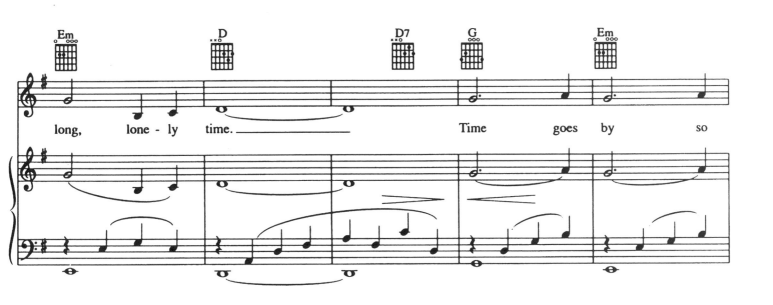

long, lone - ly time. ___ Time goes by so

Up Where We Belong
(from "An Officer And A Gentleman")

Words & Music by Jack Nitzsche, Will Jennings & Buffy Sainte-Marie

422

Tiny Dancer
(from "Almost Famous")

Words & Music by Elton John & Bernie Taupin

Moderately slow, with a beat

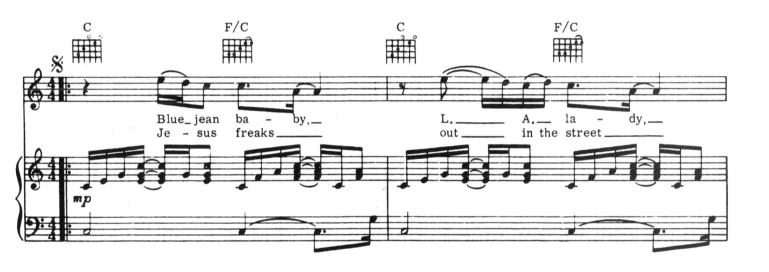

Blue jean ba - by, L. A. la - dy,
Je - sus freaks out in the street

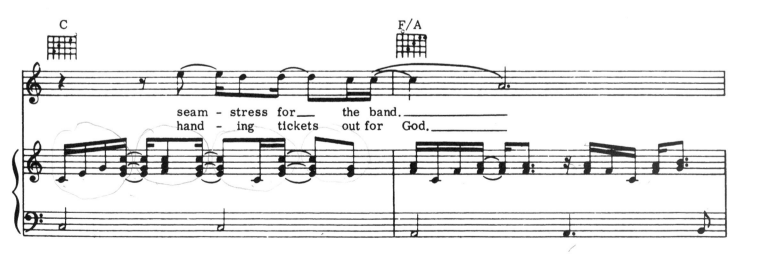

seam - stress for the band.
hand - ing tickets out for God.

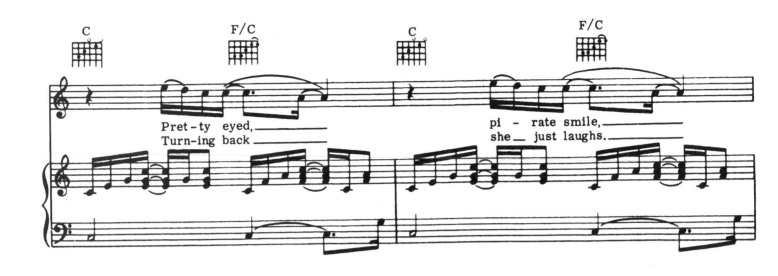

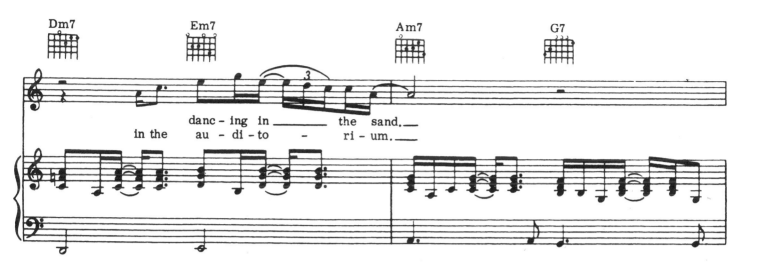

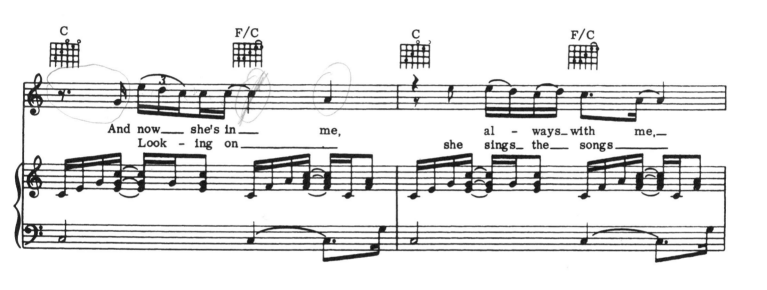

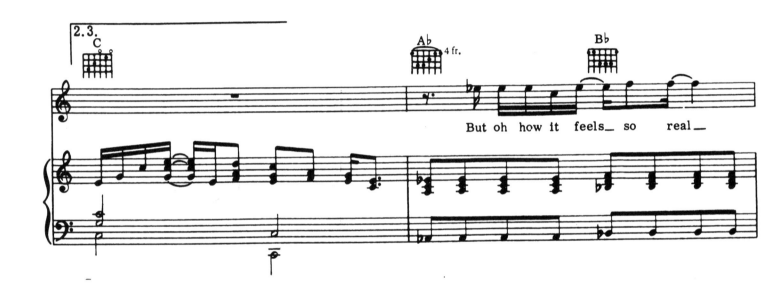

But oh how it feels__ so real__

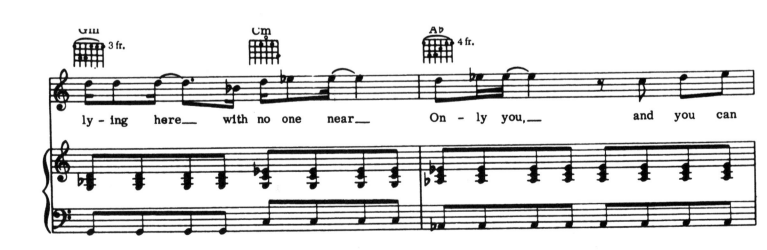

ly - ing here__ with no one near__ On - ly you,__ and you can

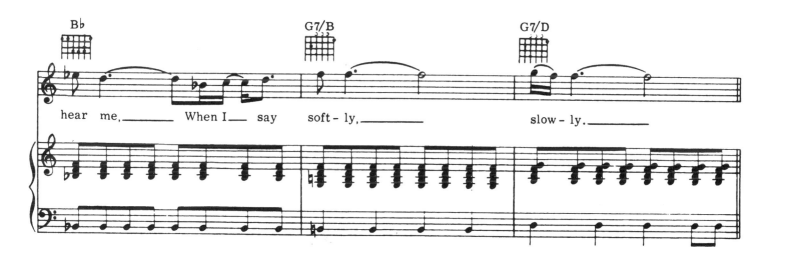

hear me,_____ When I__ say soft - ly,_____ slow - ly._____

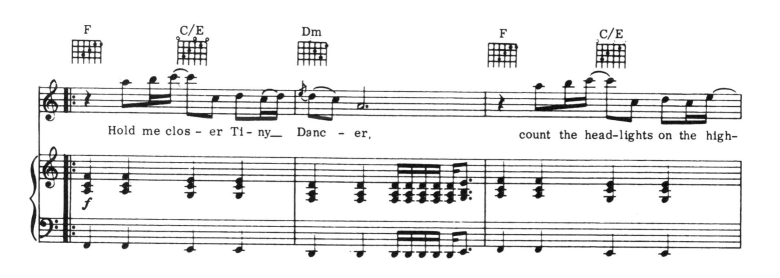

Hold me clos - er Ti - ny__ Danc - er, count the head-lights on the high-

- way._____ Lay me down__ in sheets of lin - en,

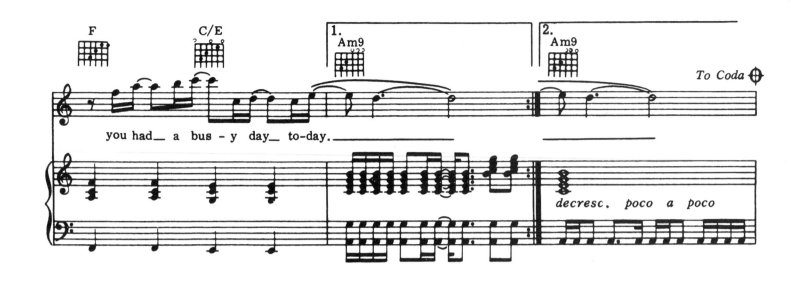

you had_ a bus - y day_ to-day._

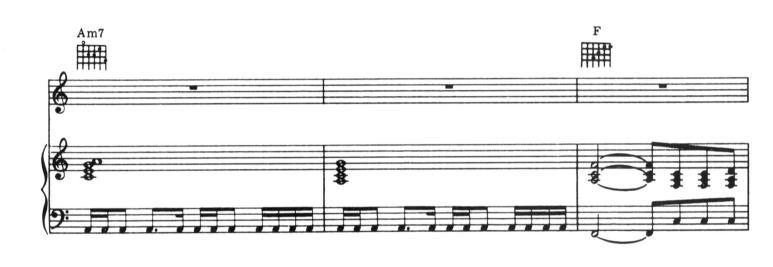

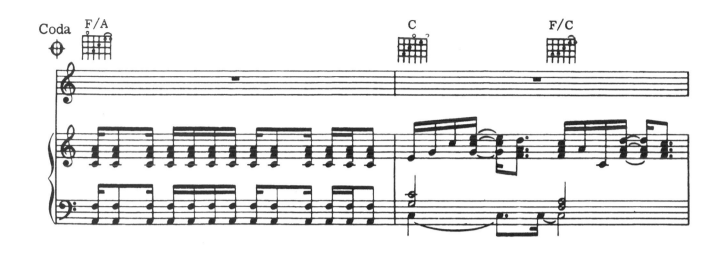

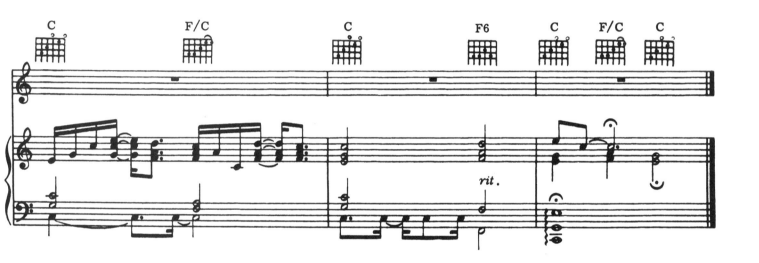

A Waltz For A Night

(from "Before Sunset")

Words & Music by Julie Delpy

Waterloo
(from "Muriel's Wedding")

Words & Music by Benny Andersson, Bjorn Ulvaeus & Stig Anderson

Werewolves Of London
(from "The Color Of Money")

Words & Music by Waddy Wachtel, Warren Zevon & Leroy Marinell

hai - ry hand - ed gent who ran a - muck in Kent,

late - ly he's been ov - er - heard in May - fair. "You'd better stay away from him,

he'll rip your lungs out Jim. Huh, I'd like to meet his tailor."

A - hoo, were - wolves___ of Lon - don. A - hoo._____

What A Wonderful World
(from "Good Morning, Vietnam")

Words & Music by George Weiss & Bob Thiele

445

What The World Needs Now Is Love
(from "Austin Powers: International Man Of Mystery")

Words by Hal David
Music by Burt Bacharach

What the world needs now is love sweet love.

It's the on-ly thing___ that there's just___ too lit-tle of.___ What the

Verse 2:
Lord, we don't need another meadow,
There are cornfields and wheatfields enough to grow.
There are sunbeams and moonbeams enough to shine.
Oh listen, Lord, if you want to know.

The Way You Look Tonight
(from "Swing Time")

Words by Dorothy Fields
Music by Jerome Kern

1. Some - day,__ when I'm awf - 'lly low,
(2.) love - ly,__ with your smile so warm
3° Instrumental

when the world__ is cold, I will__ feel a glow just think - ing of__ you__
and your cheek__ so soft; there is__ no thing for me but to love__ you__

1.
Cmaj7 Bm7 Am7 D9 4fr Gadd9 Em9 Am9 3fr C/D
and the way you look to-night.
2. You're so
and the way you look to-night.
2.
Gadd9 Gmaj9 Cm7add11 3fr F11 F7♭9
3.
Gadd9 E♭/F
B♭maj9 Bdim Cm7 3fr F9 Dm7 Gm9
With each word, your ten-der-ness grows, tear-ing my fears a-part;
Cm9 F7♭9 B♭maj9 D♭7/A♭ 4fr Cm7 3fr F13♭9
To Coda
and that laugh that wrink-les your nose

just the way__ you look to - night,__

just the way you look to - night,_____ darl - ing;

just the way you look to - night.__

When You Wish Upon A Star
(from "Pinocchio")

Words by Ned Washington
Music by Leigh Harline

Wise Up
(from "Magnolia")
Words & Music by Aimee Mann

(Verse 2 see block lyric)

It's ___ not ___ what you ___ thought ___ when you first ___ be - gan ___ it. ___ You ___ got what you ___

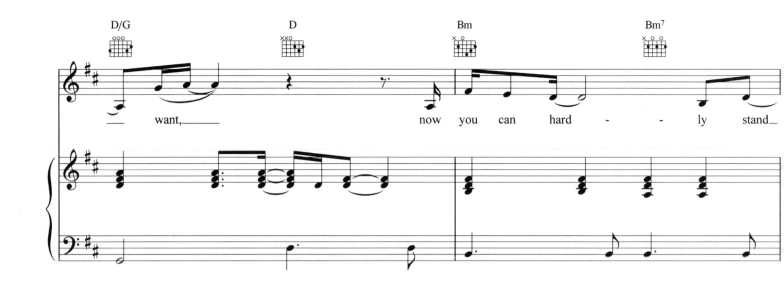

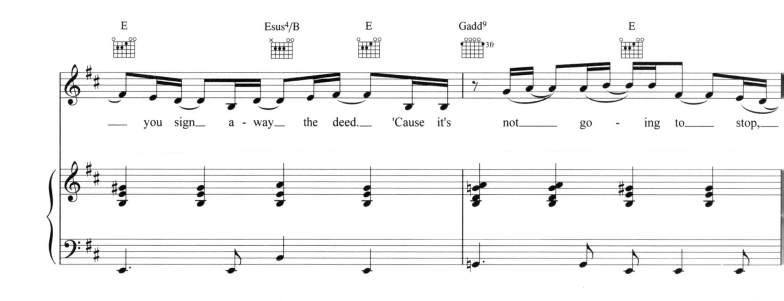

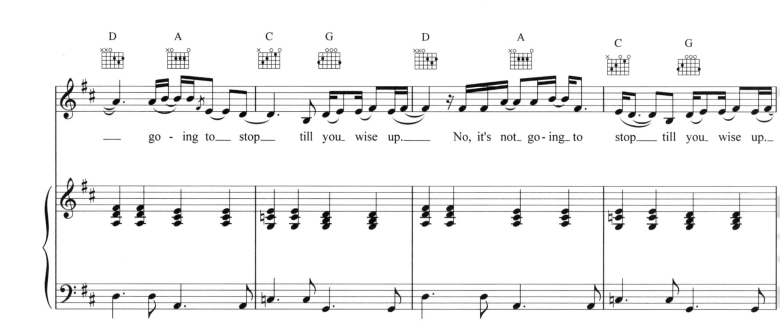

No, it's not____ go-ing____ to____ stop, so just give up.____

Repeat to fade

Verse 2:
You're sure there's a cure
And you have finally found it.
You think one drink will shrink you till
You're underground and living down.
But it's not going to stop
It's not going to stop
It's not going to stop
Till you wise up.

You Never Can Tell
(from "Pulp Fiction")

Words & Music by Chuck Berry

G7

-ly love the ma - de - moi - selle____

and now the young m' - sieur____ and ma - dame____

____ have rung the cha - pel bell____

c'est la vie,____ say the old____ folks, they

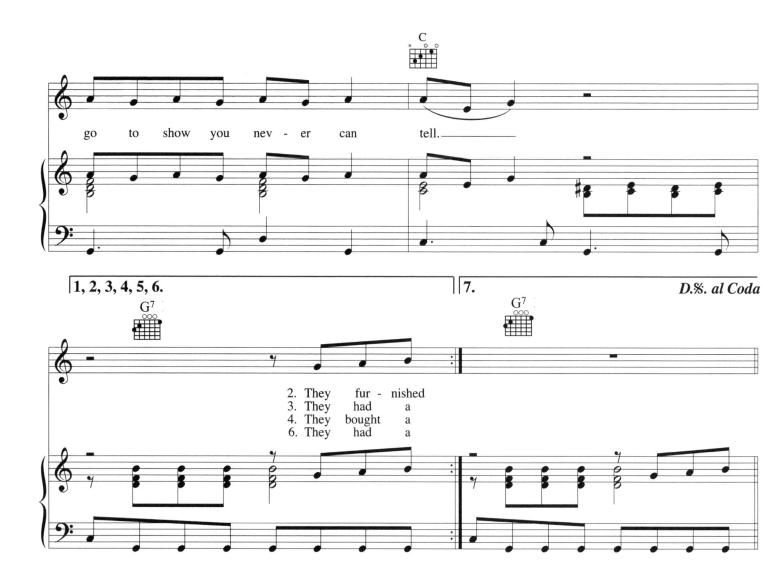

go to show you nev - er can tell.____

1, 2, 3, 4, 5, 6.

7.

D.%. al Coda

2. They fur - nished
3. They had a
4. They bought a
6. They had a

Verse 2:

They furnished up an apartment with a two-room Roebuck sale
The Coolerator was crammed with TV dinners and ginger ale
But when Pierre found work, the little money come in worked out well
C'est la vie, say the old folks, they go to show you never can tell.

Verse 3:

They had a hi-fi phono, boy did they let it blast
Seven hundred little records all rockin' rhythm and jam
But when the sun went down the rapid tipple of the music fell
C'est la vie, say the old folks, they go to show you never can tell.

Verse 4:

They bought a souped-up Jitney was a cherry-red '53
And drove it down to Orleans to celebrate their anniversary
It was there that Pierre was waving to the lovely Mademoiselle
C'est la vie, say the old folks, they go to show you never can tell.

Verse 5:
Instrumental

Verse 6:

They had a teenage wedding and the old folks wished them well
You could see that Pierre did truly love the Mademoiselle
And now the young M'sieur and Madame have rung the chapel bell
C'est la vie, say the old folks, they go to show you never can tell.

Verse 7:
Instrumental to fade

You Must Love Me
(from "Evita")

Music by Andrew Lloyd Webber
Lyrics by Tim Rice

Where do we go from here? This is-n't where we in-tend-ed to be. We had it all, you be-lieved in me, I be-lieved in you.

colla voce–accompaniment optional

(play)

2º lyric

Why are you at my side?
How can I be any use to you now?
Give me a chance and I'll let you see how
Nothing has changed.
Deep in my heart I'm concealing
Things that I'm longing to say,
Scared to confess what I'm feeling
Frightened you'll slip away,
You must love me.

You're The One That I Want
(from "Grease")

Words & Music by John Farrar

Moderately

1. I got chills, they're mul - ti - ply - in',
(Verse 2 see block lyric)

and I'm los - - - in' con - trol.

'Cause the pow - er you're sup - ply - in',

Verse 2:
If you're filled with affection you're too shy to convey
Meditate in my direction, feel your way.

I better shape up 'cause you need a man
Who can keep you satisfied.
I better shape up if I'm gonna prove
That your faith is justified.

(Are you sure?
Yes I'm sure down deep inside.)

You're the one *etc.*

You've Got A Friend In Me
(from "Toy Story")

Words & Music by Randy Newman